How to Control

MIND
and be

STRESS-FREE

How to Control
MIND
and be
STRESS-FREE

A scientific step-by-step guide to strengthen your mind, elevate your thoughts and relieve you from stress

Er. M. K. Gupta

PUSTAK MAHAL®

Publishers

Pustak Mahal®

Administrative office and sale centre
J-3/16 , Daryaganj, New Delhi-110002
☎ 23276539, 23272783, 23272784 • *Fax:* 011-23260518
E-mail: info@pustakmahal.com • *Website:* www.pustakmahal.com

Branches
Bengaluru: ☎ 080-22234025 • *Telefax:* 080-22240209
E-mail: pustakmahalblr@gmail.com
Mumbai: ☎ 022-22010941, 022-22053387
E-mail: rapidex@bom5.vsnl.net.in
Patna: ☎ 0612-3294193 • *Telefax:* 0612-2302719
E-mail: rapidexptn@rediffmail.com

© **Author**

ISBN 978-81-223-0048-2

Edition June : 2015

No rights reserved. No part of this publication may be reproduced, stored in a retrieval system or transmitted, in any form or by any means, electronic, mechanical, photocopying, recording or otherwise, without the prior permission in writing from the author/publisher.

Printed at : Radha Offset, Delhi

Preface

Although in the market many books are available on these topics, but they mostly touch their moral and spiritual aspects only without any scientific back up. They are in the form of preachings as to what you should do and what you should not.

The present book is an attempt to bridge this gap between Science and Spirituality. It first scientifically explains the nature of mind, thoughts and stress and then also suggests techniques for their control and management on a scientific basis. It also adequately explains their impact both on physical as well as mental health by clearly explaining the interaction which exists between mind and body. Fourth chapter gives some mind elevating articles which will enlighten you about realities of life and help in relieving stress.

I fervently hope that people who have scientific bent of mind will definitely like and benefit from this book. I will appreciate any comments/suggestions from my revered readers.

I may also inform my readers that now the Hindi translation of this book is also available in the name of 'तनाव मुक्त कैसे रहें' from the same publishers. Hence those wishing to have the Hindi version of the book, may avail this facility.

With best wishes

—**M. K. Gupta**
Inter-University Accelerator Centre
(Formerly Nuclear Science Centre)
J.N.U. Campus, New Delhi-110067
E-mail: *mkg@iuac.res.in*

CONTENTS

1

Mind_____

"Mind is the most powerful thing in the world. One who has controlled his mind can control anything in the world."

— Swami Sivananda

"To me the very essence of education is the concentration of mind and not the collection of facts. If I had to do my education over again and had any voice in the matter, I would not study facts at all. I would develop the power of concentration and detachment and then with a perfect instrument (mind) I could collect facts at will."

— Swami Vivekananda

INTRODUCTION

The essence of all *yogas* and spiritual education is the control of mind. It is a must not only for ascending the ladder of spiritual life but also for achieving success in our day to day practical life. *Once you control your mind, happiness and peace come as a natural consequence.*

Almost all our agonies and pains are due to our not having proper control over our mind. Instead of becoming master of our mind, we have become its slave. It makes us dance from here to there according to its whims. Instead of we dictating upon it, it is dictating on us and pulling and pushing us in various directions. *The servant has become the master and the master has become the servant. We*

9

have to restore our master status and place the servant in its proper position if we want to be really happy and peaceful again. This means that we should be able to put our minds where we want and keep it from running here and there. *Unless we contro! and overcome our mind, we are bound to be unhappy and stressed. We can't avoid it. In fact it is the difference in the ability to control the mind that makes one different from another.*

An uncontrolled mind constantly fluctuates from one thought to another. It doesn't want to remain still even for a minute. No sooner one thought goes, another thought comes and this chain never ends. Even while asleep, this restless mind is troubling us in dreams. It is crying, jumping, giving and receiving blows, etc. all the time. The more we try to fight it, the more strongly it bounces back upon us and makes us more agitated and disturbed.

An uncontrolled and unbalanced mind also gets constantly torn apart by various emotions, viz. likes, dislikes, love, hatred, jealousy, revenge, anger, grief, pride, fear etc., which are generated because of the inability of the mind to face life or world as it really is. It gets carried away by the dualities of life like gain/loss, success/failure, praise/insult, life/death, pleasure/pain, union/separation, etc. because of which it is overjoyed and excited at one moment while in the next moment it is highly frustrated, depressed, and tense.

Once you conquer your mind, you become a totally transformed person, always peaceful and cheerful. Nobody and no situation in the world can deflect you from your state of equilibrium. You reach a stage where all external circumstances lose hold over you and surrender themselves to your feet. *You can stand like a rock amidst severest opposition and obstacles.* You are

10

the king of the kings and have the power to move the whole world, if you desire so . You are a source of light and power for whoever comes in contact with you. Power of a controlled mind increases manifold in the same way as the power of running water increases when it is controlled by constructing a dam.

Although difficult yet by constant practice and firm determination, it is definitely possible to conquer your mind. It may require a life long practice but considering the rewards, it is worth.

Before starting the practice to control the mind, we must understand its basic nature and attributes. Any attempt to control the mind without understanding its basic nature and characteristics are bound to lead to failure. That is why most of the people are found saying that even after a practice of many years, they still find themselves where they were in the beginning.

NATURE OF MIND

What Is Mind

Mind is that faculty by virtue of which we are able to be conscious and aware of ourselves. Consciousness and awareness of self and others are the basic characteristics of mind which distinguish sentient or living things (having mind) from insentient or non living things (not having mind). A stone is not conscious of itself, as it has no mind. Same is the case with all physical objects. Since they have no consciousness, they can't think, analyze, reason, feel good or bad, sense pleasure or pain. It is the mind which thinks, reasons, analyzes, discriminates, feels good or bad, senses pleasure and pain, imagines and worries etc. An inanimate object doesn't have all these faculties.

11

Your mind or soul is the real you. Your body is in your possession just like you possess a house, a car; that is why you refer to the body in the same way as you refer to your car or house, i.e. my body, my car, my house etc. The body is the instrument of mind through which it (mind) acts in the world and also suffers or enjoys.

It is the mind which sees, hears, smells etc. through respective sense organs and through the mechanism of the brain. It is the mind which feels the pleasures or pains of the body. If mind is off or disconnected from the body, you will feel no pain. For example, while sleeping a person feels no pain of a physical injury because at that time his mind is dissociated from the body. It is also the mind which speaks, eats and works through respective physical organs (*Karmendriyas*).

Mind Is Different from the Brain

The brain is a physical organ like any other organ of the body while mind is a non-physical entity. The brain can be compared with a sophisticated computer through which mind controls and connects itself to the body. Thus the brain acts as a link between the mind and the body.

Thinking, reasoning, feeling, imagining etc. are all attributes of mind only. The brain as well as the body being physical and inanimate by nature, can't think or feel. The body and the brain are made alive and animated by the entry of mind or soul only. At the time of death, when mind (or consciousness or soul) leaves the physical body, the brain as well as the body fall dead and become like any other physical object of the world. The brain and the body, thus, are simply instruments of the mind.

12

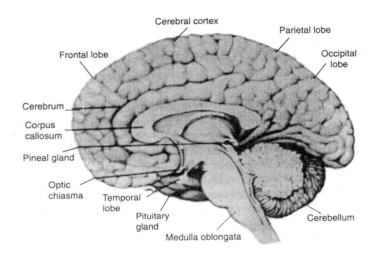

Cerebral cortex
Parietal lobe
Frontal lobe
Occipital lobe
Cerebrum
Corpus callosum
Pineal gland
Optic chiasma
Temporal lobe
Pituitary gland
Medulla oblongata
Cerebellum

Brain is a physical organ. Non-physical mind or consciousness resides in it.

Mind Has No Weight or Measurement

Being non-physical, mind can't be weighed or quantified in any measurement nor can it be chemically analyzed in any laboratory. These are all the attributes of physical objects only.

Mind Is Eternal and Immortal

The brain and the body, being physical in nature, are subject to decay and are perishable in nature, while mind or consciousness or soul never dies. It survives the death of the physical body. With the passage of time, mind, instead of decaying, grows with the experience and maturity. To put in short, mind or soul is without a beginning, or an end. It is immortal. There was never a time when it was not there and there will never be a time when it will not be there. It is beyond creation and dissolution, beyond time and space and is eternal. No external violence, murder, fire, accidents or bombs can touch it.

13

Mind Is Indivisible in Nature

Like physical things, mind or consciousness can't be divided into parts or pieces. It acts as a whole. Some persons think that the mind or soul of a child is created out of the mind or soul of parents. This is absurd because as explained earlier, consciousness is not a physical thing and can't be dislodged from parents' consciousness as pieces. Similarly some persons think that Supreme Soul (God) has divided Himself into various parts which have become individual souls. The idea itself is absurd and doesn't fit in any logic.

Mind Is Self Luminous and Self Energized

Unlike physical objects which require a source of energy, mind or consciousness doesn't require any outside energy to function. It is self energized and self luminous, and goes on functioning till eternity. It is the brain which needs energy for its functioning.

Mind Can Exist Independent of the Body

Mind is much superior to the body. Mind acts as a master and the body as the servant of the mind. After death the body dies, but the mind continues to exist as one's basic identity.

There are some persons who develop their mental powers to such an extent that during their life time itself, they can leave their body at will and travel as far as they like and then come back to their body. During this travel, they (i.e. their minds) remain connected to their body by a fine silvercord. This is called 'out of the body experience' or 'Astral travelling'. Sometimes we can have this experience without any conscious effort when we have a near miss with death or near death experience.

In the event of death, this silvercord gets broken so that the body and mind become totally separated and the body falls dead.

14

There are other mental powers, e.g. telepathy, clairvoyance (perceiving distant scenes by mind), clairaudience (listening to distant sound by mind) etc. In all these phenomena, body or our physical senses are not involved. These phenomena are directly manipulated by our mind only.

Also during deep stages of meditation one becomes totally oblivious and detached from one's body. At that stage if someone talks to you or touches you, you don't notice it because mind has almost disconnected from the body and the outer world, and has turned towards the inner world.

Location of Mind in the Body

Mind or soul is a subtle point of light that resides in the middle of the forehead between the eyebrows (called '*bhrikuti*'). In yogic language this place is also called '*ajna chakra*'. The custom of putting a red dot called '*tilak*' at this particular spot on the forehead is indicative of the importance of this place. Some people have a wrong belief that the seat of soul is in the heart and that all our emotions come from our heart. Seat of the soul is

Here resides the mind or consciousness

15

in the brain because it is through the brain that it connects to the whole body. Brain functions like a control room of the body from where soul, sitting like an operator, controls the whole body. All our emotions also originate from our mind or soul only. Heart is a physical organ which regulates the blood circulation in the body. A physical thing can't generate emotions which are non-physical in nature.

Mind and Body Influence Each Other

Mind and body are very closely interlinked. Any change in the state and health of the body influences the state and health of the mind. Similarly any change in the state or mood of the mind has a corresponding physiological response in the body. *In other words we can say that mind and body act and react on each other. Nevertheless the effect of mind over the body is much more than the effect of the body on mind.*

Yoga explains this great inter-relationship between mind and body through an intermediatery which is called 'prana'. Prana is also called vital force or vital energy which supplies energy to the physical body for its functioning through a network of *'nadis'* spread throughout the body which are invisible by physical eye.

Prana radiates out of the body upto some distance and can be seen as an *'aura'* around the body by clairvoyant vision. It can be seen to some extent by special physical methods. In fact *'prana'* is neither totally physical like the body nor totally non-physical like mind. It can be called a sort of semiphysical entity.

Prana on one side is connected to the body and on the other side it is connected to the mind. *Any disturbance in the balanced and perfect state of the body leads to imbalance in the flow of prana which in turn affects the*

16

balance of mind since prana is also connected to the mind. Disturbance in the balanced state of the body can come due to many reasons e.g. faulty diet, overexertion, overlaziness, overindulgence in sensual pleasures, faulty style of living, environmental conditions, over medication, and use of drugs etc.

Similarly, on the other side any disturbance in the balanced state of mind creates imbalance in the flow of *prana* which in turn affects the health of the body since *prana* is connected to the body also. *Disturbance in the balanced state of mind can be caused by various negative emotions and vices in mind like hatred, jealousy, anger, greed, revenge, ego, attachment to worldly things, selfishness etc.*

In medical terminology, the same thing is explained in the form of balance between two components of autonomous nervous system, namely sympathetic nervous dystem and parasympathetic nervous system. The balance between these two components get disturbed if there is an imbalance created either in the body or in the mind.

However as you rise higher and higher on the spiritual ladder, you reach to a level, where you can make your mind totally immune to bodily afflictions and sufferings. You attain that degree of control over mind that you can detach it from the body at will and thus not get affected by it. Further at that level, your power of tolerance and mental strength increases to such an extent that you can cheerfully bear a pain which will otherwise break a normal person into pieces.

LEVELS OF MIND

There are three levels of mind which together give the mind a single identity.

17

Conscious Mind

Conscious mind is that part of our mind which reasons, thinks, discriminates, contemplates and analyzes. Emotions or feelings of all sorts, i.e. likes, dislikes, love, hatred, jealousy, anger, joys, sorrows etc., are all experienced in this mind. Imagination of all sorts of future happenings and worrying about the past are all done through this mind.

According to *Raja Yoga,* conscious mind consists of three faculties—Lower mind (*Manas*), Intellect (*Buddhi*) and Ahamkara (sense of I-ness).

Through physical senses (sight, sound, smell, touch and taste), conscious mind remains in contact with the outside world. All voluntary movements of the body are done by our conscious mind through the respective organs of action (*karmendriyas*).

Besides, the conscious mind also remains in touch with the subconscious mind (another level of mind described later). Impulses and urges from our subconscious mind induce the conscious mind to behave in a certain way and to indulge in certain types of action. However, the conscious mind on the other hand is also subject to pressures from society and outside world which expect it to act or behave in a certain way so that its image is not tarnished. It results in a conflict if the subconscious mind's urges and the social expectations don't match and thus our conscious mind remains in a state of conflict and turmoil. If it increases too much, it results in many psychosomatic diseases.

The central idea in mind control is to remove this conflict in the conscious mind by exposing the subconscious mind totally and removing all types of biases, prejudices, fears, suspicions, and negative emotions (like anger, greed, jealousy, revenge, hatred) stored there.

Subconscious Mind

Subconscious mind is another level of mind and is accessed when we go deep inside our inner journey.

The subconscious mind is the storehouse of our memory. All that we have ever seen, heard, thought, talked, done whether in this life or earlier lives get stored here as a sort of permanent record. Emotions linked with our thoughts, words and actions are also deposited in our subconscious mind along with memory. It is this emotional part of our thoughts/words/deeds which after depositing in the subconscious mind plays havoc with us. These emotions make the conscious mind restless by constantly agitating it from below. They are like fire balls kept below the conscious mind. The urges and impulses rising from the subconscious mind, constantly demand satisfaction through the conscious mind.

Pure memory without any emotions doesn't affect the purity of subconscious mind. It is the emotions which make the water of subconscious mind impure and turbulent and which in turn agitate the conscious mind.

Every incident to which we react with emotion also creates an impression on the subconscious mind which is called *samskara*. Because of these impressions or *samskaras*, we all have different types of predispositions, inclinations, habits, biases, phobias, fears etc. In the science of mental control, the subconscious mind is purged of all these *samskaras* and impurities, and rendered pure. To illustrate it with an example, suppose you have had a very bad experience with a tenant in your house. You had frequent quarrels, shouting, and exchange of abuses with him. By such repeated incidents, you might develop a bias or impression in your mind that now you will never give your house on rent to anybody because all tenants would be like that only. Similarly another person who has had a wonderful relation with his tenant, might develop a bias that it is good to keep a tenant in the house. *Thus, because of biases, both the persons are not able to see the reality as it is.* However, the fact of the life is that there are both good and bad persons in the world and just because some persons are bad, everybody doesn't become bad. Even you may have to stay at a place as a tenant where you do not have a house of your own, Will you behave in the same way as your tenant behaved with you? Certainly not. *The requirement is to clean the subconscious mind of all biases and past conditioning so that it can look upon the things in a completely objective way without adding the colour of emotions.*

Normally, the subconscious mind can't be directly accessed. Way to go to it is only through the conscious mind. But a branch of science has been developed called 'hypnotism' through which the hypnotist makes a direct access to his subject's subconscious mind by bringing his conscious mind in a semi-sleep or drowsy state by suitable techniques. The advantages of this direct access is that the subject's phobias, fears, biases, guilt complexes stored in the subconscious mind can be directly known and then counter suggestions can be given to the patient's subconscious mind to alter these patterns. So many psychological treatments have been done this way where the roots of the problems were lying in patient's subconscious mind. Use of hypnotism has now been extended to painless surgeries and childbirth by giving the patient necessary suggestions during hypnosis and there is no need to give external anaesthesia.

All our mental powers or occult powers belong to the domain of the subconscious mind. Telepathy (mind to mind communication), clairvoyance (seeing distant things), clairaudience (hearing distant sounds), hypnosis, autosuggestion, visualization, all these phenomena belong to our subconscious mind. When by any means (e.g. meditation, hypnosis), we have access to our subconscious mind, we can have access to these powers also. Power of materialisation of thoughts also belongs to the domain of the subconscious mind.

Functioning of autonomous nervous system in our body is totally under control of the subconscious mind, e.g. activities of breathing, digestion, blood circulation, heart, immune system, etc.

Superconscious Mind

Superconscious mind is our real self devoid of any impurity and full of bliss and peace. If we can have a glimpse of it even for a moment we will be filled with indescribable peace. It is like drinking from the fountain of joy and peace. The more we are able to stay at this place, the more the nectar of bliss and peace we can have. In fact what we call everlasting peace and happiness comes by our contact with this real self. The illusory happiness or pleasures which we derive from worldly possessions and sensory enjoyments are only short lived and mixed with pain.

Now the most vital question is how to remain in contact with our superconscious mind or real self? The subconscious mind acts as a barrier between the conscious mind and the superconscious mind and does not allow the conscious mind to perceive the superconscious mind directly by turning within. To illustrate it with an analogy, the subconscious mind is like

21

a lake filled with water, the superconscious mind is the bottom of the lake and the conscious mind is the perceiver looking from the top through the water of the lake. So long as the water of the lake is dirty and turbulent (i.e. the subconscious mind is full of impurities), the conscious mind can't see the bottom of the lake. But when the water of lake is pure and calm (i.e. a pure subconscious mind purged of all impurities), you can clearly see the bottom of the lake.

Hence in other words, techniques of self realization are nothing but a process of cleaning the impurities of the subconscious mind and a process of stilling the conscious mind and turning it inward. When the conscious mind is directed outwards, it is in contact with the world and when it is inwardly directed it is directed towards this real self (or the superconscious mind). This is what is done in meditation to turn the direction of mind inwards, that is, towards the real self.

WHAT IS SOUL

All these levels of mind, put together, constitute the soul. Therefore mind is not different from soul. In fact mind, consciousness or soul are the same things. In some religions and faiths, the superconscious mind is termed as 'soul' or 'self' while the conscious mind is usually denoted by 'mind'. It is all a matter of terminology. However, it should be clear, irrespective of whatever terminology we use, that the mind is an integral part of soul and is not an entity different from soul. Existence of soul apart from mind or consciousness has no meaning since consciousness is the basic attribute of soul which is expressed through operations of mind. There is a famous quote by an author "I think therefore I am." If you can't think, feel and have no awareness about

22

yourself (i.e. you don't have mind), then what is the meaning of the existence of a separate soul. We can also say that soul is our real 'I' or the basic identity. Body is simply a possession of soul and not our true identity. That's why we use such terms as my body, my head, my brain.

STATES OF CONSCIOUSNESS

Waking State of Consciousness

There are various states in which your mind or consciousness can express itself. When you are wide awake to the world around you thinking, analyzing, reasoning, feeling about things, you are said to be in a waking state of consciousness. In this state your conscious mind is fully active and alert.

Altered State of Consciousness

There are other states of consciousness in which your conscious mind goes to sleep or semi-sleep/drowsy state and your subconscious or unconscious mind becomes active. In some states your subconscious mind also becomes still. They all are called 'altered states of consciousness' (ASC). Some of these are described below :

Dream State: Here your conscious mind goes to sleep but subconscious mind remains active.

Deep Sleep State: Here both your conscious and sub-conscious mind are at rest.

Hypnotic State: Here your conscious mind is lulled into semi-sleep/drowsiness by a hypnotist through his special techniques and then he takes control of subconscious mind of his subject and gets many useful past information from it and then corrects the behaviour of his subject by implanting new suggestions in the subconscious mind.

Self-Hypnosis: In self hypnosis, instead of an external hypnotist, you yourself become the operator of your subconscious mind. Here you still your conscious mind (by various techniques) to have an access to your subconscious mind and then you give useful suggestions to your subconscious mind to correct various behavioural deficiencies in you. In this operation, you fully remain aware of yourself unlike the other states of consciousness as mentioned above where you lose your consciousness in the process.

Meditation: In meditation also, first you still your conscious mind and then the subconscious mind, and finally reach the superconscious state with full awareness. Please note that in deep sleep also, both conscious mind and the subconscious mind are quiet but since you have no awareness, you slip into an unconscious state rather than to the superconscious state.

By using various drugs also, you can change the state of your consciousness. These drugs act on RAS (Reticular Activating System) part of the brain which is concerned with your waking, sleep etc. and accordingly bring your conscious mind to a drowsy state. These drugs have various side effects and they weaken your mind.

But it is to be noted that once we are proceeding in the direction of mental control, we should normally strive for those states of consciousness where we remain aware of ourselves or in other words we remain under full control of ourselves. This helps in strengthening our mind. But in those states where we become passive and leave ourselves to the control of others, we are not strengthening our mind. Rather we are weakening it making it susceptible to others' influences.

24

STATES OF MIND AND BRAIN WAVES

Scientists have discovered that the brain emits electrical waves of varying frequencies in different states of mind. This frequency can be measured by a device called E.E.G. (electroencephalograms).

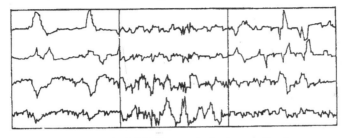

Fig. 3 : A typical E.E.G. sample during meditation

For example when we are wide awake and busy in worldly activities, brain waves are of the frequency of 14 to 21 Hz and are called beta waves. When we are quite relaxed, frequency of brain waves is between the range of 8 to 13 Hz and are called alpha waves. When we are in dreams, the brain wave frequency is between the range of 4 to 7 Hz and they are called theta waves. When we are in deep sleep, the brain wave frequency is between the range of 0-3 Hz and they are called delta waves.

Interestingly, when we are meditating and as we go deeper and deeper, the frequency of brain waves goes on reducing as described above and although we remain completely conscious during meditation, we can still reach to delta level during deep meditation. During mild meditation, we remain in alpha state. Hence through the observation of frequency of brain waves during meditation by the above referred device, depth of meditation a meditator has reached, can be known and corrective steps then can be taken to improve the quality of meditation leading to the improved health of mind.

25

MIND CONTROL & ITS METHODS

Metaphorically, it is said that you can stop the wind from blowing, you can stop the river from flowing, but you can't control your mind. Control of mind is certainly the most difficult (and also most rewarding) thing in the world, but it is possible by constant practice and adopting proper techniques.

Some persons directly advise advanced meditation techniques to the aspirants for controlling the mind but persons having highly scattered and turbulent mind find this direct meditation more difficult because they are not able to still their mind even for a moment. Result is that they feel more restless during meditation session and want to get up from meditation as soon as possible.

That's why such persons should start controlling the mind employing physical methods which don't require total stoppage of thought processes and require only mild concentration and then gradually they can shift to more arduous techniques of mental control. All these methods are described below:

Physical Methods

These are developed on the principle that mind and body are closely interlinked and once you control the body, mind is also controlled.

Yogasanas and **Exercises:** Perform *yogasanas* and various stretching exercises. By stretching various muscles, tensions deposited in them are released leading to free flow of *prana* which leads to quietness and control of mind. When muscles are tense and contracted, *prana* is not able to move freely and this has corresponding effect on the balance of mind, because mind and *prana* are closely interrelated. Similarly aerobic exercises involving rapid movements, release pockets of tension deposited in the body here and there and lead to better flow of prana and better functioning of the mind.

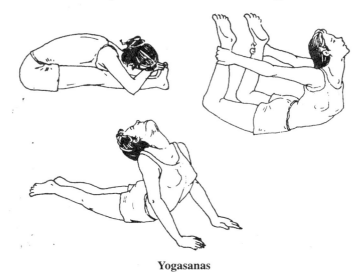

Yogasanas

Pranayama (**Breathing Exercises**): Mind and breath have a very close interrelationship. When mind is disturbed, breath also becomes irregular, unrhythmic, jerky, noisy, shallow and limited to upper chest only. When mind is calm, breath is slow, deep, rhythmic and abdominal involving movement of diaphragm. This relationship of mind and breath is also seen vice versa, i.e. by changing our breathing so as to match it with a relaxed state of mind, we can calm our mind.

By various *pranayama* exercises and '*kumbhak*', '*pranashakti*' is tremendously increased which leads to tremendous control and strength of mind. '*Nadi shodhan pranayama*' is specially effective for the balance of mind and nervous system. The reader is advised to refer to an appropriate book on '*pranayama*' for learning various techniques of breathing.

1. Holding your right nostril shut with the edge of your right thumb, inhale to a count of eight through the left nostril. Then place your index finger against your left nostril and hold your breath for a further count of eight.

2. Release your thumb from the right nostril and exhale to a count of eight, keeping your index finger on the left nostril. Then begin inhaling again through the right nostril, reversing the sequence. Repeat the two rounds five times.

Nadi Shodhan Pranayama

Kriyas **(purificatory techniques) :** These *kriyas* are also a part of *yoga* and consist of *neti* (*jal neti, sutra neti*), *kunjal, tratak, kapalbhati, vasti, dhauti*. These have been specially designed to clean the impurities of the body. Once the impurities of the body are removed, *prana* flows freely and mind becomes calm and quiet because of its interrelationship with *prana*. Readers are advised to consult an appropriate book on *yoga* for details.

Jal Neti

28

Sitting Postures : In *yoga* various sitting or meditative postures have been described with a view to specially calm the mind for meditation. These postures are such that once you master them, you can sit effortlessly in them for a long time. In these *asanas* your spine becomes straight and correctly aligned. To name a few such postures they are *padmasana, siddhasana, swastikasana, vajrasana, sukhasana* etc.

Sukhasana

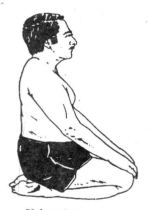
Vajrasana

Once we sit in these postures unmoved for a certain period of time, we find that mind has become centred and controlled. Why ? First, because in the motionless state of body, mind also becomes quiet because of its interrelationship with the body. Secondly the straight vertical spine encourages *prana* to rise upwards against its normal tendency of going downwards during other activities. *When prana rises upward in spine, mind not only becomes calm and quiet but achieves a higher level of consciousness and its strength and control are greatly enhanced.*

Diet: Diet has a great influence on mind. In *yoga*, three types of food are described - '*satwik*', '*rajasik*' and '*tamasik*'.

29

By eating *satwik* food, *prana* flows properly in the body and mind also remains quiet, positive, and under control. Examples of such foods are fruits, vegetables, milk, honey, lemon, yoghurt, dry fruits (nuts), whole grain cereals etc.

Rajasik foods are those which stimulate the mind and make it restless e.g. tea, coffee, tobacoo, cigarette, cola drinks, sugar, salt etc.

Tamasik foods are such which make the mind dull and lethargic e.g. meat, stale foods, onion, alcohol, fatty foods etc.

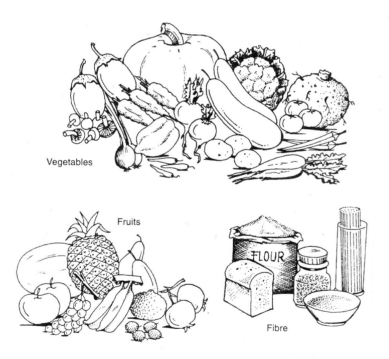

Vegetables

Fruits

FLOUR

Fibre

Satwik *Foods*

In addition to the type of food, it also matters when we eat, how much we eat, what combination of foods we eat and at what temperature we eat. For example too hot or too cold food is not good for the system.

Fasting: Fasting also leads to the control of mind by two reasons. First, during fasting, the body's impurities are removed which leads to a balanced flow of *prana*. Secondly, one has to exercise his will power not to succumb to the temptation of food. It results in the development of mental control and strength.

Celibacy is an important factor in the control of mind. One who wastes his sexual energy indiscriminately can't control his mind. However 'Celibacy' here doesn't mean total abstinence from sex as people misinterpret. Sex is a natural biological urge and its forceful suppression may create many physiological and psychological problems.

What is meant in the present context of celibacy is that you should not become slave to this urge. You should enjoy it like a master and shouldn't allow it to control you. You should constantly remember that you are bigger than sex and sex is only a tool in your hand for getting pleasure and for procreation but it can't be bigger than you. So while you should enjoy it but at the same time should not get overly attached and identified with it and should maintain your superior status compared to sex. Our scriptures say **'Enjoy the world but not let the world enjoy you. You may eat food but not let the food eat you.'** Vital energy preserved through judicious control of sex helps in the upliftment of mind.

'*Om*' and '*gunjan*' Sounds: These sounds have been found to be very effective in controlling and calming a distracted and disturbed mind, because of the powerful

31

effects of vibrations generated by them. For making '*om*' sound, inhale deeply and then exhale slowly through the mouth making the sound 'O'. Make this sound as loud and as lengthy as possible. At the end, close your lips making 'M' or humming sound. In '*gunjan*' sound, inhale deeply through both the nostrils and exhale slowly through the nose only, making the sound of humming like a bee from the throat while keeping the lips closed.

Trataka: '*Trataka*' is a very effective *yogic kriya* for strengthening and centering the mind. It is done by gazing at a certain object continuously with open eyes till tears start trickling down. The object may be a candle flame, a dot on the wall, a flower or the picture of a deity or any thing on which you can easily focus. You can sit either on ground or on the chair with spine, neck, and head straight and the object should preferably be at a distance of 3 feet. *Trataka* is also very good for strengthening and removal of impurities of eyes.

Trataka on candle flame

Silence: Silence is a very effective tool for increasing mental power. A lot of energy is dissipated during gossips, arguments, discussions and unnecessary talks. By silence we conserve mental energy. Practically it is

32

not possible to remain silent all the time. Hence we should earmark at least some time in the day when we can remain in total silence. During this time we can read, write and listen to some soothing slow background music.

Environmental Conditions: In addition to all the above, it should also be ensured that the environment around you is conducive to good mental health. For example noise levels, climatic conditions (temperature, humidity, ventilation, sunlight), colours and the neatness of surroundings affect the mental health. The negative environmental conditions can sometimes neutralize one's efforts in the direction of mind control.

Mental Methods

In these methods the will power is used to change certain aspects of the personality as mentioned below. After following physical methods of mind control, it will be easy to exercise such will power.

Concentration: *As physical exercises increase the strength of the body, similarly concentration improves the strength of mind.* Strong mind is not easily affected/ disturbed by trials and odds of life. For improving concentration, whatever activity we are engaged in, we should try to be totally absorbed in it, however trivial it may be. At that time, except for this activity (and things associated with it), the whole world should be dead for us. For example, even if we are eating a fruit we should completely relish each morsel of fruit with our attention totally directed to it. If we are bathing, we should enjoy this activity deriving maximum benefit from it by keeping our attention totally anchored to it. Similarly, while reading a book we should be totally absorbed in it oblivious of any other thing. One should also learn to concentrate on uninteresting things to develop real control of mind. Concentration in other words, also means to learn to remain in the present moment which is a very desirable feature for success and happiness in life. Normally it is seen that people remain engrossed either in the past memories or in future anticipations and don't remain in the present fully and thus the power of their concentration is weakened.

Detachment and Forgetfulness: Alongwith concentration, we should also develop the ability to detach ourselves from anything or any task at a moment's notice. Some people can concentrate and absorb in a task but they find it difficult to forget this first activity completely while taking on to the next activity. They have some hangover period. This only shows that we get unduly attached with various things which we should not.

Please note that the world is a great training school. The only importance of various worldy things and incidents is to give us necessary training and lessons for our growth. They themselves are not important as such.

Hence we should use them for our learning and growth but should not get attached to them. Once the purpose is served by learning necessary lessons, we should forget and discard them. Concentration and detachment should be practised simultaneously. This is what Swami Vivekanand also stressed. Ability to forget and detach from undesirable past is a great quality for achieving success in life. It is well said *'Though it is sometimes useful to remember but it is often wise to forget'.*

(*Note*: Strictly speaking nothing is forgotten, everything gets stored in our subconscious mind. What we mean by the word 'forgetting' here is that we should not consciously bring that thing to our conscious mind again and again.

Planned Thinking: It should be ensured at various intervals that thinking is planned and systematic, and not haphazard and random. *Unplanned random thinking and day dreaming are a sign of weak mind* and indicate that instead of controlling the subconscious mind, one is being controlled by it. The conscious mind should remain fully active, in full awareness and should maintain its master status controlling his servant (the subconscious mind). By going into passive, idle and day dreaming state, the influence of subconscious mind increases on the conscious mind. Therefore one has to ensure that only those thoughts are in the mind which are really wanted at the moment. It has been noted in a survey that a sizable portion of one's life time is spent in wasteful thinking. This time can be easily utilised to perform some useful activities.

Positive Thinking and Change of Mental Attitudes: *We give the least importance to this most important aspect of our life, i.e. how we think. It is the single largest factor in building up of our personality and character.* One should develop the habit of viewing everything positively, even the most miserable situations should be

35

viewed thus. Negative thinking weakens the mind, makes it restless, agitated and impure. Convert every negative situation into positive by readjusting your mental attitude. To give an example as to how it should be done, suppose someone abuses you or makes some undesirable remarks in anger, then instead of feeling bad about him, just think that his mood is upset or he is still not fully mature; that is why he behaved like that. But don't develop any malice against him. This is positive attitude.

By having positive thinking, you will also attract favourable physical conditions and environment. As per the law of psychic attraction, you attract physical conditions and circumstances towards you according to your thoughts. To give an example, suppose you repeatedly think of not catching a particular disease, you will find that symptoms of that disease start appearing in you. Such is the power of thought. It is as real as that of a solid stone.

By remaining positive, you create an aura of positive vibrations around you which not only benefit you but also all others coming in your contact. This aura also protects you from the attack of any negativity released by others.

Control over Impulses (Self Restraint and Patience): In your daily life, don't get driven by the impulses. It is a sign of weak mind. Have some checks and controls on your mind and don't become its slave. Be the master of your mind. Whatever impulse or urge comes in your mind (it comes from your subconscious mind where these tendencies, desires, passions lie in dormant states), don't oblige it immediately. First examine it properly and then accordingly hold it for sometime or ignore it totally. By exercising patience in this manner, your will power and strength will increase gradually.

For example, suppose it comes to your mind suddenly that you should eat '*golgappa*' or '*chat*'. There are two courses open to you. One is to rush immediately and satisfy your lust, another is to hold a check on your mind and examine by intellect as to how much it will be reasonable to rush instantly to five miles. By adopting the second course you increase your will-power. You should try to exercise such type of patience everywhere and avoid hurry, anxiety and desperation for worldly matters and sensual pleasures. You should also exercise tolerance and patience in the face of people's remarks, insults or criticism about you instead of reacting immediately. This also increases the strength of your mind.

Spiritual Methods

Meditation (*Raja yoga*): Last but not the least, key to the control of mind is meditation. In meditation, you shut off your mind from the outside world and turn it inwards. This is done by some special forms of concentration in which you focus your mind on a single point or stimulus. This process quietens the mind and turns it inwards. In this state of mind, the subconscious desires, impurities, and emotions become activated and start rising to the surface of consciousness. You witness them like a spectator and they are released from

Meditation

your consciousness. Gradually your subconscious mind is purged of all impurities, emotions, desires, phobias, passions, fears etc. and becomes clear like a crystal. In this state you can clearly see your real self (or superconscious mind) and drink as much nectar of peace, bliss, power as you want. At this stage you are a self realized person with a complete mastery over your mind. No external condition or circumstance can disturb the balance of your mind. You rise much above the petty worldly things. You are like a lotus flower blooming happily in the sludge of world.·

Constant Remembrance of God (*Bhakti yoga*): Whenever you remember God, a sort of invisible link is established between you and God by virtue of which the flow of peace, purity, bliss, knowledge, and power starts descending on you from God and this gradually purifies and strengthens your mind. The more you live in a state of God consciousness, the more speedily your mind gets purified because of the flow of above mentioned attributes. The technique of constant remembrance of God is to try to feel His presence while talking, eating, walking, sleeping, travelling as if you were eating with him, travelling with him, talking with him, sleeping with him.

Mind connected to God while working

Whatever you do, feel God be in front of you. Involve him in all your activities. Make Him

38

your partner in everything you do and never feel yourself alone. Try to do and understand everything in terms of God. This is how an aspirant in the path of *'Bhakti yoga'* cleanses his mind and finally achieves God realization. It is said that at those moments when a person is in remembrance of God, he is a very powerful person having direct link with God and one should be very careful in imparting any harm to him.

Unselfish Action (*Karma yoga*): Doing actions selflessly as a part of one's duty also leads to purity of mind. You consider each work as an order from the divine and perform it sincerely and with dedication as a servant of God considering God as the real doer. There is no consideration of any personal gain. You do it as a service to God and service to world. This attitude leads to complete purification of mind.

Knowledge of Self, Supreme Self (God) and World (*Gyan yoga*): This is another way to enlighten the mind, which mainly suits to intellectuals. It deals with study, contemplation, discussion, and enquiry to understand the true nature of oneself, God, and the world. Once you come to know the truth and mysteries of life, all your doubts, fears, complexes, and anxieties are dissolved which lead to complete purification of the mind.

❏ ❏ ❏

2

*Thoughts*_____

What you call the atmosphere of your home or office
is not dependent upon its building material or its
furnishings. The atmosphere is a register of the
quality of the thoughts of those who dwell there. It
will be harmonious in measure that courtesy,
goodwill, good temper, and kindness are permitted
to rule the minds of the residents or occupants.

                              — St. Anselm

I hold it true that thoughts are things
Endowed with bodies, breath, and wings.
And that we send them forth to fill
The world with good results or ill.

                       — Ella Wheeler Wilcox

Life's battles don't always go
to the stronger or faster man.
But soon or late to the man
Who think he can.

                                — Virgil

INTRODUCTION

One of the most important aspects of our life is our
thought process. All our actions and behaviour have their
origin in our thoughts. Thoughts are not ordinary things.
They are potent weapons which can injure others and
therefore should be handled very carefully. It will not
be an exaggeration to say that thoughts are the greatest
forces in the world acting on mankind, although invisible
in nature.

NATURE AND EFFECTS OF THOUGHTS

In fact every thought acts as a mould in which our future is being constantly shaped. Hence it is very desirable for an evolving soul to understand correctly the nature of thoughts and their effects and powers so that, they can be controlled to the best of their advantages. The following points make an humble attempt in this direction.

Thoughts Have Vibrations: As there are vibrations of lights, sound etc. similarly there are vibrations of thoughts. Whenever we think some good or bad thoughts, vibrations of these permeate in the surrounding atmosphere and affect the people present there positively or negatively depending upon the nature of thoughts. In other words the atmosphere gets charged with the thought vibrations present there.

Thought Vibrations Are Different from Physical Vibrations: It is also to be noted that thought vibrations are not physical in nature like vibrations of light and sound etc. They are non-physical in nature. Physical vibrations (like that of light and sound etc.) are felt by our conscious mind directly through our physical senses, while thought vibrations are first registered in our subconscious mind and from there the impression is passed on to the conscious mind. That is why you can't apprehend thought vibrations so clearly as physical vibrations. Thought vibrations being non-physical can also not be quantified in any measurement like physical vibrations.

Thoughts Have the Power of Materialization: Whatever we think, we attract physical conditions and events in accordance with it. By a mysterious process, our subconscious mind tends to materialize all our thoughts into their physical equivalent by the most direct

42

and practical media available. More the power of thought, more the power of materialization. The power of thought increases by repetition of the same thought again and again by attaching emotions (e.g. love, faith, expectancy etc.) with the thought. If your thoughts are positive, positive conditions will emerge in life. If your thoughts are negative, negative conditions will emerge in life. The subconscious mind doesn't make any distinction between good or bad thoughts. It will just accept any thought whether good or bad transmitted to it by our conscious mind and starts executing it like a faithful and the most powerful servant of the conscious mind.

Thoughts Hit the Person Against Whom They Are Directed (Principle of Telepathy and Thought Transference): Powerful thoughts directed to any person are like a force acting upon him. When you are actually thinking good or bad about a person you are not doing an ordinary thing. You are actually hitting that person by your thoughts and that person actually feels that effect, depending upon the power of your thoughts (which depends upon the concentration of your thought and the emotions linked with that thought) and the receptivity of that person (i.e. how much the other person's concentration is directed towards you). Emotional part of your thought hits like a solid stone to the other person to whom your attention is directed.

Thoughts hit the person against whom they are directed

43

Let us understand a little more about the phenomena of thought transference or telepathy. When we direct our attention or imagination towards a person, we become connected to him on the mental plane. More the concentration and better the visualization of that person in our mind, the better we are connected to him mentally and better will be the telepathy in this condition. Hence depending upon our rapport with another person on mental or astral plane, we can influence him by our thoughts.

When many persons combinedly transmit their concentrated thought upon somebody, the effect is tremendous. If these are negative thoughts, the other person feels as if a bomb is exploding upon his head. If these thoughts are positive, he feels elevated.

Thought Transference Is Independent of Time and Space: There is no time and space in the realm of thought and mind. Whether a person is sitting in the next room or the other corner of the world makes no difference as far as telepathy is concerned. Mental connection in both the cases is just the same and distance makes no difference in receiving and giving message.

Thoughts Are Constantly Modifying and Affecting Our Subconscious Mind: Whatever we think, it goes on depositing in the vast lake of our subconscious mind. We are constantly depositing good and bad impressions in our subconscious mind according to the thoughts we are harbouring. Accordingly this lake becomes dirty or clean. Impressions of these thoughts in our subconscious mind further incite us to have similar thoughts off and on again. So this becomes a vicious circle that needs be broken. By various *yoga* practices and deliberate positive thinking, the negative impressions of our thoughts can be gradually erased leading to the purity of mind.

This should make it clear that thoughts should not be treated as a small matter. Ordinarily people think that their thoughts cannot be known to others and nothing will happen just by thinking. But you have seen that *every thought makes a groove in our subconscious mind and becomes a part of our overall personality. Personality is nothing but a sum total of all impressions deposited in our subconscious mind.*

By Harmful Thoughts, We are Activating the Law of *Karma***:** By harbouring any ill feeling (like hatred, jealousy, revenge, dislike etc.) against anybody we are actually doing a bad *karma* or '*vikarma*' as per *karma* philosophy and we will get suitable punishment in future for this, according to the law of *karma*.

Hence every thought makes a definite impact upon our future and once released, it can't be so easily erased from the storehouse of our *karma*. It is stored like a permanent record.

None of Your Thoughts Is Hidden: You may apparently hide your thoughts from your friends, colleagues and give them a twisted version by your words, but Omniscient God is watching each and every thought of yours on a moment to moment basis. Nothing is hidden from Him who is our real and spiritual father. He only matters to us ultimately because our relationship with Him is permanent while with others it is temporary. *Everything will leave us one day except God.* A person who has awakened his telepathic faculty, can also read your hidden thoughts.

A Strong and Positive Mind Remains Immune to Negative Thought Vibrations: A strong and positive mind is a sure antidote to any negative thought vibrations or psychic attacks. It has a strong aura which can't be pierced by negative thought vibrations. Negative thoughts directed towards such a person rebound without affecting him. One can increase his mental strength and positivity by the practice of yoga, concentration, and deliberate attempt to keep oneself positive in daily activities.

Thoughts Attract Like Thoughts: Our atmosphere always remains filled with all sorts of thought vibrations. Whenever we think something, we attract similar types of thoughts from the thought atmosphere, according to the law of psychic attraction. For example, if you are thinking anything bad, you will be surprised to see so many other associated bad thoughts hovering in your mind. Similarly, if you are thinking something good, you will be astonished to find so many other good thoughts and ideas suddenly appearing in your mind. This can make it clear as to how a bad thought can make you further worse and how a good thought elevates you further.

Negative Thoughts Weaken Mind and Make It Restless: Negative thoughts weaken your mind and make it restless, agitated and impure while positive thoughts strengthen it and make it pure. Hence, it is not a question of just thinking a thought. *Each thought is making a definite impact upon the health of your mind also.*

Positive Thinking Creates a Positive 'Aura' around Your Body: Aura is radiations or emissions around your body and their quality depends upon the state of your health and state of your mind. If your mind is always positive, cheerful and peaceful, the quality of your *aura* will be very good. This *aura* or auric vibrations benefit not only you but also all those who come in contact with you. A tired and restless mind feels a soothing effect in

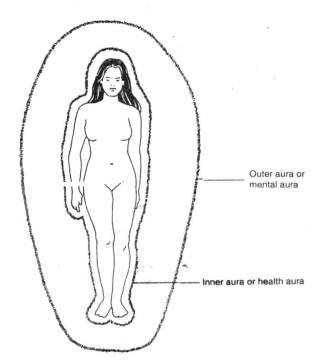

Outer aura or
mental aura

Inner aura or health aura

The nature of human aura

the vicinity of such persons in a similar way as a thirsty man feels relieved after reaching a source of water. Here the difference between auric vibrations and thought vibrations should be clearly understood:

• Thought vibrations occur only when you think of something while your auric vibrations are always there even when you are not thinking, e.g. in deep sleep or deep meditation. In fact in deep meditation, the quality of your *aura* and its width increases instead of decreasing.

• *Aura* is limited to only certain width around the body, say 1-2 feet, while thought vibrations spread in larger distance, depending upon the intensity of your thoughts and emotions attached with it.

47

• Quality of your *aura* depends upon your character in general and on specific emotions which are present in your mind at a particular time, while quality of thought vibrations depends only upon the thoughts released at a particular time.

Your *auric* vibrations and thought vibrations constantly influence and modify the atmosphere you live in or move around. Conversely your aura also gets on being modified depending upon as to which places and among which persons you usually spend your time. For example, if you spend sometime in a spiritual *ashram* and among holy people, it automatically has a modifying influence on your *aura* and you become a transformed person effortlessly.

Thoughts Create Thought Forms: Whatever we think, a thought form is created in the atmosphere according to what we are visualizing. More the power and concentration of thought, more sharp and clear the thought form will be. A clairvoyant with his astral vision can perceive this thought form.

When our thoughts are coupled with emotions, emotional part colours the thought form positively or negatively. For example, when a person shows anger, irritation, hatred, the thought forms around him in the atmosphere are so ugly (like black clouds of smoke) that if you can percieve them with your astral vision, you will feel that you are in a hell. Similarly, positive and pure emotions of love, care etc. create pleasing thought forms.

For how long a thought form will survive, depends upon the force of your emotions behind it. They (thought forms) disintegrate and fade after a certain time when their energy is exhausted. Some strong thought forms which are reinforced continuously can exist for a very long time even after their originator has expired. Persons coming into the way of these thought forms feel their definite impact upon them.

Your Thoughts Tend to Induce Similar Thoughts in Others: This is also called the law of thought induction, according to which thoughts released by you tend to induce similar thoughts in others. Negative thoughts of hatred, jealousy, anger, and greed produce similar thoughts in others who are in the immediate vicinity of that person. Similarly a cheerful and positive person can fill the whole atmosphere with cheerfulness by his thoughts which can transform even a gloomy and depressed person into a cheerful person for the time being. However it is true that a strong and positive minded person will not be so much affected by negative thoughts as a weak minded person will be.

Negative Thoughts Produce Strees Response in the Body While Positive Thoughts Create Relaxation Response: Negative thoughts not only disturb your mind they also create stress or alarm response (also called fight or flight response) in the body because of which certain biological changes occur in the body system due to arousal of the sympathetic nervous system. If this happens frequently or constantly due to one's habit of indulging in negative thoughts, continuous imbalance is created in the two components of autonomous nervous system (namely sympathetic and parasympathetic nervous system) which leads to stress and so many psychosomatic diseases.

In *yogic* terminology, the same thing is understood in this manner that when your mind is negatively charged, the flow of *prana* gets disturbed and disturbance in the flow of *prana* leads to physical disorders or diseases because the physical body is sustained by *prana* only.

49

On the other hand positive thoughts create relaxation response in the body tending to bring physical parameters to more balanced conditions. Positive thoughts increase your *pranic* energy and direct it upward in the body which helps in your enlightenment while nagative thoughts deplete the *pranic* energy of the body and turn its direction downwards in the body which takes man more away from his goal of enlightenment.

Thought Vibrations Also Influence Physical Objects: Thought vibrations released by you or the auric vibrations around you tend to stick and influence the quality and purity of the physical objects which are in their vicinity. For example the clothes you wear, or the chair you sit, the pen you use, all carry your vibrations. Any person touching or using these objects, which you use frequently, will also take some share of these vibrations and will be influenced positively or negatively. Your vibrations also go with the food you cook or serve, in fact with everything you possess or deal with. However vibrations which are taken on by physical objects go on getting modified depending upon how many persons are using them and by the influence of various physical factors such as heat, sunlight, air, washing, or boiling a thing in water, painting etc.

There is a branch in Occultism called psychometry in which experts of psychometry can tell your character just by touching a thing which you often wear or use, by getting in touch with your vibrations through that object. In fact this is the reason as to why you feel so uplifted and purified when you touch the objects used or possessed by a great soul because you happen to be in touch with vibrations of that soul through that object. On the contrary you feel horrified when you enter into a room of a wicked soul or use the objects possessed by a wicked soul.

When You Think About a Place, You Are Affected by Thought Vibrations of That Place: As soon as you think about a person or a place, you are mentally transported to that place and are affected by the vibrations around that place or person. If that person and place is good, you will receive good vibrations. If that person or place is bad, you will receive bad vibrations. Hence your psyche will be polluted or purified accordingly. That's why it is said that not only in actions but in thinking also you should be dwelling on good things only otherwise you may be unconsciously doing a lot of harm to yourself.

HOW TO MODIFY THE THOUGHT PROCESS

After learning the basic nature and laws relating to thoughts, we should also ponder over a little as to what a person should do in order to improve his thought processes.

There are different ways and means to control and regulate our thought process. Following are some important ways:

Avoid Random and Haphazard Thinking: Ensure at various intervals that your thinking is planned and systematic and not haphazard and random. Unplanned random thinking and day-dreaming are signs of a weak mind and indicates that instead of controlling your subconscious mind (that part of mind where all your urges, desires, inclinations lie stored) you are being controlled by it. Your conscious mind should remain fully alert, in full awareness and maintain its master status controlling his servant (the subconscious mind). By going into loose, idle, and day dreaming state, you encourage the

51

influence of the subconscious mind on your conscious mind. So ensure that only those thoughts are in your mind which you really want to think at the moment.

Make Deliberate Attempts to Remain Positive at All Times: It is the single largest factor in building up of our personality and character. We should make a deliberate attempt in our daily life to view everything positively, even in the most miserable situations. As soon as a negative thought comes to your mind, convert it into a positive one by readjusting your mental attitude. (It has been explained in the previous chapter also).

Reduce Emotional Elements in Your Thoughts: There are emotions (e.g. likes, dislikes, love, hatred, fear, revenge, jealousy etc.) coupled with our thoughts which are playing havoc with our life. The root cause of our emotional involvement is that we take worldly problems and difficulties very seriously. Remember that various trials and tests you are facing in life are coming to you according to a certain law. Nothing in this world happens by chance or by accident. There is a reason for everything which is happening to us or others. Also remember that everything which happens to us is for our good only, however cruel it may appear. Nothing is designed in the universe to harm us. All these trials and tests are to teach certain lessons to us which we have not yet learnt. They (trials) are not permanent. They are all temporary and will pass away having served their purpose.

If we consider these trials and difficulties as burdens coming to us out of nowhere, we are simply making the matter worse and prolonging our release from the problems. In fact when you evolve spiritually, you will realize that you yourself are responsible for what is happening to you. You only had created certain causes in past which are now germinating in the form of effects.

Hence use all trials and tests of life as opportunities to learn something instead of cursing and blaming others and never lose balance of your mind and thoughts in whatever miserable situations you are. Observe all your problems like a spectator and solve them with a detached and unbiased mind.

Be Consistent in Your Thoughts, Words and Deeds: Be consistent inside and outside. Your thoughts, words, and deeds should show resemblance with one another. This is the true test of a righteous person. Normally it is seen nowadays that people have two faces. One is their real face and the other is false one to show to others. Their inside and outside don't match. This type of duality of behaviour disturbs the stability of your thoughts.

Conscious Relaxation: Off and on whenever you find time, practise conscious relaxation. This is achieved by shifting awareness of mind from thought process to pure perception or pure awareness. For example you can perceive or gaze the photo of your deity or any other pure symbol. Remember, you are simply gazing and there are no thoughts involved in it. Similarly you can concentrate on a pleasing sound. Here again you are only perceiving or hearing sound with full awareness but the usual chattering of thoughts inside the mind is stopped. You can also concentrate on your breathing (observing each incoming and outgoing breath inwardly with closed eyes). *In all the above processes mind is fully active but there is a shift of focus from thoughts to pure awareness.*

This state stops the agitation and restlessness of the mind and you achieve clarity and relaxation of mind which helps in subsequent thinking and contemplating with clarity. *This state of mind also produces 'relaxation response' in the body and body is also relaxed.*

Practice of *Yoga* and Meditation: One should also resort to the practice of *yoga* and meditation. If done correctly the process of meditation gradually resolves all the conflicts of the unconscious mind and makes the mind pure and strong. Once the mind is pure, you are bound to project positive and pure thoughts only. A strong and pure mind has full control of its thoughts and doesn't become restless and disturbed as easily as a weak and impure mind. When your unconscious or subconscious mind is rendered pure by melting of all its '*samskaras*' by fire of meditation, you can also perceive your Real Self or Divine Self very clearly which is the source of all bliss, peace and power.

❏ ❏ ❏

3

*Stress*_____

No man's life is free from struggles and problems, not even of the most powerful and wealthy, but everyone may build up his own happiness by making himself independent of outward conditions.

— Humboldt

Outer circumstances and events don't create stress. It is our response to them which creates stress.

— Swami Rama

NATURE OF STRESS

What is Stress?

Technically, whenever we perceive anything as a threat to us whether physical or psychological, we are under the grip of stress. However from a practical or lay person's point of view, whenever our mind feels uneasy, restless, disturbed, agitated, tense, heavy, or strained, we are said to be under stress. On the other hand, when our mind is feeling light, easy, cheerful, calm, and quiet, we are said to be in a relaxed state, opposite to that of stress.

It is interesting to know that our each mental activity is associated with a physiological response from the body generated through the action of our autonomous nervous system. To understand stress completely it is very essential to know about it.

Effect of Stress on Body

Whenever we experience stress, a stress mechanism is activated which is also called 'fight or flight response or alarm response'. It is as if a red alert is declared in the body to meet the impending challenge or emergency. In this condition the sympathetic component of autonomous nervous system is aroused through an impulse from the hypothalamus leading to the following body responses.

- Pituitary gland releases the hormone ACTH which triggers the adrenal glands.

- Adrenal glands produce another hormone cortisol which acts on the liver.

- Cortisol converts glycogen stored in the liver into blood sugar to provide instant energy.

- Breathing becomes faster to provide more oxygen to the body.

- Stress chemicals such as adrenalin and non-adrenalin are released directly into the blood stream to produce a surge of energy in the body.

- Heartbeat is increased to increase blood circulation.

- Blood vessels are dilated and blood pressure is increased.

- Sweating increases, skin resistance decreases.

- Muscle tightness and tension are increased to enable them to be ready for action.

- The process of digestion is shut down as blood is diverted away from stomach towards skeleton muscles.

- Dilation of pupils occurs to allow more light into the eye.

- Mouth dries up, because the salivary glands dry.

- The rectum and bladder muscles relax.
- Shaking of the limbs, cracking in voice.
- Blood is diverted away from the skin. Peripheral blood vessels are constricted giving a feeling of coldness in hands etc.
- Immune system becomes weak.

All the above changes in body chemistry occur basically to provide extra energy to the body to meet the impending challenge.

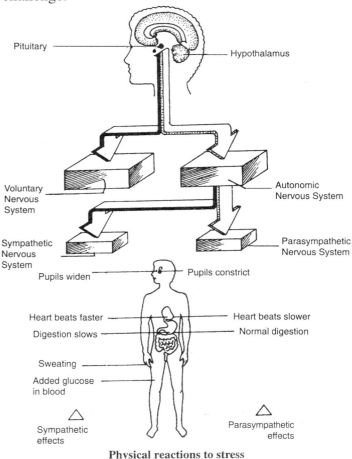

Physical reactions to stress

57

On the other hand when we are peaceful, relaxed and not aroused, the other branch of autonomous nervous system, namely, parasympathetic nervous system takes over. Its function is more or less opposite and complementary to SNS (sympathetic nervous system). It makes body chemistry return to normal by balancing the sympathetic response. Sympathetic is action oriented and aggressive involving muscular exertion and large expenditure of energy. Parasympathetic is restoring and passive. It is concerned with internal housekeeping, relaxation, and restoration of the body like repair of tissues, inward activities of nourishment, and excretion etc. Ideally the SNS and PSNS work in a balanced and complementary fashion so that activation and relaxation alternate each other.

Every Sympathetic Arousal Is Not Stress

Although stress creates sympathetic arousal, every sympathetic arousal is not stress. For example when you want to run for the improvement of your health, your sympathetic nervous system is aroused to give you extra energy for running but you are, nevertheless, not under stress. In fact every motor action (involving physical organs of action or '*karmendriyas*') arouses sympathetic nervous system to a lesser or higher degree.

Stress occurs only when there is excessive or prolonged sympathetic arousal causing an imbalance between sympathetic and parasympathetic nervous system. Hence the more correct definition of stress is that 'stress is a state of autonomic imbalance'. *Consequently we can have periods of arousal (or patterns of activity) that are healthy and non-stressful as long as they are balanced by periods of relaxation and rest. Prolonged stress is a consistent pattern of imbalance resulting from the habitual dominance of sympathetic (fight or flight response) activity or parasympathetic (possum response) activity.* Stress also occurs when the energy developed by SNS arousal is not used or released and gets bound up in muscles as tension e.g. when you are mentally anxious and agitated but there is no physical action.

Over Inactivity or Lethargy (Overparasympathetic activity) also Creates Stress

Increased parasympathetic activity is also harmful for the body because it again creates a state of autonomic imbalance and results in a different kind of stress. In other words, *a state of relaxation (parasympathetic dominance), if it is not balanced by activity, can also become dysfunctional, resulting in lethargy, passivity, withdrawal and depression.* There are a significant number of individuals who even respond to threat with passive withdrawal or what may be called the parasympathetic or possum response. That is instead of preparing to fight or run away when faced with a threatening situation, they just roll over and play dead. Their response to fear is not arousal, but inhibition. This is marked by the typical characteristics of parasympathetic discharge — decreased physiological functioning, loss of skeletal tone, mental lassitude, inactivity, and eventual depression. This possum response may be originally rooted in the failure of autonomic arousal to adequately cope with the perceived threat. Certain diseases like asthma and duodenal ulcers, are directly assoicated with abnormal parasympathetic activity.

Hence, to repeat the fact that we have either arousal or inhibition doesn't mean that we have stress. The key element in defining the physiological parameters of stress can be whether or not there exists a balance between sympathetic and parasympathetic activity.

59

When Does Stress Result in Disease?

Sympathetic arousal which occurs under stress, draws on the body's available resources in order to provide extra energy to meet the challenge. If the sympathetic nervous system is continuously activated due to constant stress (worries, concerns, fears etc.), the body's resources are depleted. This results in exhaustion, disease, breakdown, and sometime even in death of the organism. Sustained or intense parasympathetic dominance also leads to disease and death but in a different way. Parasympathetic dominance doesn't lead to depletion of bodily resources but rather to a failure to utilize these resources.

Following is a brief list of diseases which are stress related. It is said 80% of diseases are due to stress. They are either originated or aggravated by stress and are called psychosomatic diseases :

(1) Asthma (2) Back pain (3) Digestive disorders, stomach ulcers, diarrhoea (4) Headaches, migraine (5) Spondylitis (6) High blood pressure (7) Arthritis, rheumatism (8) Diabetes (9) Muscular tightness (10) Various mental disorders including fits.

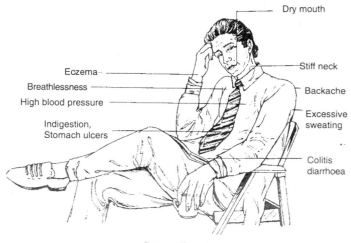

Stress disorders

60

Which of these diseases one will catch, depends on the weaker zones in your body which will be the first target of attack.

Effect of Stress on Performance and Behaviour

As explained earlier, sympathetic arousal is a necessity to meet demands and challenges made on us. In fact as arousal increases, we perform better. It is only over arousal or under arousal which interferes with performance. Individuals who remain constantly overactivated (or in other words 'stressed'), their performance suffers. Clearly the best solution is to match activation to the task at hand.

Similarly due to excessive parasympathetic response (reflected in over laziness, passivity), some people remain underactivated and they also can't give appropriate performance.

In fact this overactivation or underactivation is only what is termed as stress. Appropriate arousal for doing something and similarly appropriate rest after arousal or activity are normal requirements.

The effect of overactivation on our general behaviour is that we easily become upset, irritated and impatient. We become confused and fickle minded in taking decisions. Our concentration and memory weaken. Our anxiety increases. Other behavioural patterns include:

- Leaving important tasks undone until the very last minute, then panicking and being unable to complete them.

- Allowing insufficient time to get to work and to important appointments.

- Trying to do two or more things at the same time and always remaining under time pressure.

- Working and reading while eating.

- Talking too fast, too loud or too aggressively, swearing, interrupting others, or talking over them, not listening to what people have to say and arguing for the sake of it.

- Not able to sit quietly at one place for a long time, moving here and there in a tense jerky way.

- Losing sense of humour.

- Reacting nervously or irritably, loosing control over their reactions and unable to cope calmly; overreactive behaviour.

- Accident prone driving on road.

- Insomnia (sleeplessness) and restless sleep, sleep walking.

Stress Addiction

There are some people to whom it becomes their second nature to always remain in a condition of arousal. They are always moving, tensing, planning and worrying. The habit of restlessness becomes so deeply entrenched in them that it seems unnatural to them to allow their body and mind to relax. Chronic tension and restlessness of both mind and body simply become their habit. They are always racing against time and are constantly under time pressure. They purposely seek out high stress situation and stress inducing behaviour. Their bodies generate greater quantities of stress hormones than normal to maintain their mental and physical 'high'. These people are called stress addicts. Simply because they adapt to such a lifestyle doesn't mean that they will be spared from the wear and tear of stress. Unconsciously they are gradually being eaten away by stress without becoming aware of this until the day when they notice some outward signs of a stress related illness or start feeling exhaustion, fatigue and eventual collapse of their body. Similarly the persons who remain habitually in a state of under arousal (parasympathetic response), also get the share of its harmful effects as already described.

The principal way we can guard against this stress addiction is to become more aware and sensitive to the signals and signs of stress with respect to behaviour and functions of our body.

Physical Signals of Stress

There are outward signs by which we can guess or judge that a person is in stress, for example :

• Biting nails.

• Clenching fists.

• Clenching jaw.

• Finger tapping on chair/table.

Typical Stressful Face

63

- Grinding teeth while sleeping.
- Hunching shoulders.
- Wrinkles on forehead and tense forehead muscles.
- Frequent sighing or yawning (indicates stress of lethargy).
- Tapping feet on the floor.
- Shaking while sitting on chair.
- Shallow breathing or upper chest breathing.
- Tightness in muscles of various parts of body like lower back, neck, shoulders, upper back, thighs, calves and feet muscles, arm muscles, facial and forehead muscles.
- Tightness of stomach and reduced movement of diaphragm.
- Loss of appetite.

One may exhibit some or many of these symptoms depending upon his stress prone habits to which he is hooked to.

CAUSES OF STRESS

Stressors (which cause stress) can be broadly placed in the following categories:

Psychological or Mental Stressors: Psychological causes of stress revolve around the fact as to how we mentally react to various events and problems around us and how we look at the world and life in general. If we react to various things around us with negative emotions (like anger, fear, hatred, jealousy, revenge, worries, irritation, frustration, anxiety), they are bound to create stress. To illustrate, suppose there has suddenly been some problem in your car. One way is to feel highly tense as to why it has happened. Another way is to take it as a way of life; that is, you are ready to accept any eventuality in life.

Hence psychological causes of stress can be very easily eliminated by readjusting your attitudes and reactions to various things of life. *Events or various incidents themselves don't create stress, it is only our attitude and outlook towards them which create stress. If we can learn to view everything in a positive way, it is impossible to be in stress.*

(*Note:* Readers are advised to read my other book titled '*How to Remain Ever Happy*' for more light on the change of various mental attitudes).

Environmental Stressors: Example of environmental stressors are excessive cold, excessive heat, excessive noise, excessive humidity, pollution (smoke, dust, harmful chemicals) in the air and water, improper lighting, over crowding etc. All these things make us stressed and activate the stress mechanism. How much we get affected by environmental stressors, depends on our body resistance or stamina or in technical parlance '*prana shakti*'. That is why different people seem to be affected in different degrees under the same environmental conditions, some get totally exhausted while others may still be able to manage.

Physical Stressors: Physical stressors are those which are related to our body and way of living as mentioned below.

(a) Faulty Diet: Certain types of food increase our stress levels like excess intake of white sugar, salt, coffee, tea, alcohol, drugs, cola drinks, sweets, chillies, spices and pickles, meat, cigarettee, tobacoo etc. They activate the stress mechanism by stimulating SNS.

An example of environmental stress: Urban crowding especially on cramped public transport is a major stress factor in modern life

Many drugs and foods can cause stress

Note: To know more about the harmful effects of various foods on body and mind, please read our book **'Foods that are Killing You'** by the same author.

(b) Faulty Breathing: Similarly our breathing habits tend to influence directly the autonomic nervous system and thereby influence our stress response. If our habitual breathing is shallow (limited to chest), rapid, jerky, noisy and is not rhythmical, slow, and diaphragmatic (from abdomen), we are unconsciously activating our stress response because such a breathing is characteristic of a stressed state of mind.

(c) Faulty Postures: Our postural habits, play a vital role in contributing or activating our stress levels. The way we stand, sit, walk have a great influence on our stress level. For example if we sit with a straight spine, we feel confident and energetic but if we sit with a curved spine and rounded shoulders, we will feel lazy, lethargic and bored.

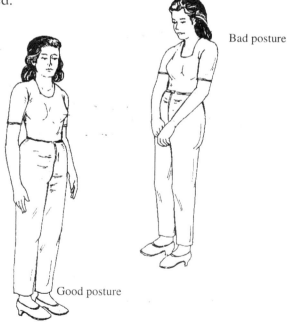

Bad posture

Good posture

Bad posture and good posture

Note: To understand more about good & bad postures, please read our book **'Freedom from Cervical & Back Pain'** by the same author.

(d) Diseases: If we have a disease or chronic health problem, it also contributes to stress, because a disease means some imbalance in the system which is likely to create uneasiness in the mind also. In fact body and mind are so intimately connected that specific blockages in the body system (or more appropriately the blockage in the flow of energy or *'prana'*) create specific patterns in mind like some diseases perpetuate anxiety, some may create fear in mind, some may cause anger and irritation, some may cause depression and nervousness, some may create a gloomy state and sadness in mind etc.

However by reacting negatively to any physical disease or environment stressors, we further aggravate our stress level. Hence by controlling our negative reaction we can stop further aggravation of stress.

(e) Excessive Speaking/Talking: Excessive talking also results in overstimulation of sympathetic system. There is a lot of expenditure of nervous and muscular energy when you speak. In fact one hour of continuous speaking may tire you more than even 5 hours of physical labour because the number of muscles involved in speaking is much more than the muscles used in physical labour. So excessive talking may also lead to stress. This is why so much emphasis is laid on silence for mental peace and dissolution of stress.

(f) Overexertion: Over exertion also leads to stress because of continuous overarousal of sympathetic nervous system which leads to an imbalance between the two components of autonomous nervous system (SNS and PSNS).

DISSOLUTION OF STRESS

Obviously the way to dissolve stress which has accumulated through the constant arousal of sympathetic nervous system, is to counter this effect by consciously increasing the parasympathetic response. The techniques which help in achieving this, are called conscious relaxation techniques and their main focus is to return the body chemistry to normal and to soothe the tightness in muscles which has occurred due to constant deposition of energy there whenever we have experienced stress emotions (e.g. aggression, impatience, anger, anxiety, fear etc. all of which kindle the body's stress response).

Relaxation Techniques

Meditation: In meditation we quiet our mind by various techniques which give a chance for parasympathetic system to dominate and thereby slow down all the bodily functions which were previously aroused.

Stretching Exercises: By stretching various muscles, the pockets of tension and tightness are released and thus muscles get relaxed which were previously tight due to stress response.

Stretching exercises

Note: To know more about various stretching exercises, please read our book **'Freedom from Cervical & Back Pain'** by the same author.

Aerobic Exercises : Aerobic exercises requiring rapid movements of body also help in releasing the bound up energy in tight muscles by utilizing this energy for movements and thus provide relaxation to body and mind. Aerobic exercises also stimulate release of endorphins (body's natural pain-killers) in the body which gives a pleasant feeling to mind.

Aerobic exercises

Massage : In massage therapy, by gradual pressing and releasing the muscles, muscles get loosened and their tightness and tension vanishes which lead to physical relaxation. By gliding the hands on the body in the form of long and short strokes, the tired and frayed nerves are also pacified.

Accupressure: In accupressure therapy, by pressing various points in the body located in hands, feet, face, spine, the energies in the body (also called 'prana' in yogic terminology) are balanced. By balancing this basic energy, all imbalances in bodily functions including tightness of muscles are removed leading to relaxation.

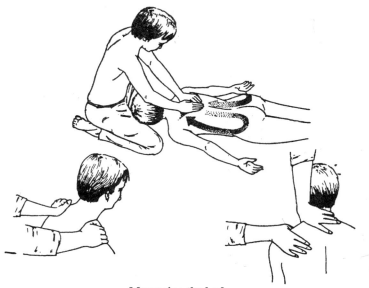

Massaging the body

Relaxing Effect of Water and Other Nature Cure Methods: Water acts as a great relaxant for a tired and tensed body and mind. There are various techniques in hydrotherapy for giving variable benefits but the relaxation obtained **by a simple hot or** cold water bath itself

Relaxing effect of water

71

convinces us about the great relaxation property hidden in water. Hot water, in principle, relaxes the muscles while cold water invigorates and soothes the tired nerves. Floating in a swimming pool/lake water with a letting go feeling is very calming and relaxing after a tiring day. The lightness of the body felt during floating also lightens the mind. Similarly other nature cure methods like fresh air bath, sunbath, mudbath also have potential for giving relaxation to us.

Yog Nidra: In *yog nidra*, we rotate the consciousness or mind through various body parts. Wherever consciousness is directed, more *prana* flows to that part of the body and imbalances are removed from there. Hence by simply directing our attention or mind inwardly (eyes closed) on various body parts, we can also relax our body. If it can also include auto suggestion (i.e. to mentally suggest that part of the body to relax) along with the concentration of attention, the effect will be more enhanced.

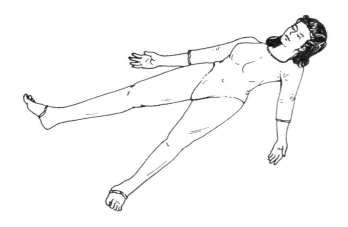

Yog nidra

Abdominal Breathing: Breathing has a very deep and subtle relationship with the state of our body and mind. If our body and mind are tense, our breathing will be rapid, shallower, jerky, non-rhythmical. Similarly if our body and mind are relaxed, breathing will be slow, deep, rhythmical and diaphragmatic (i.e. from abdomen).

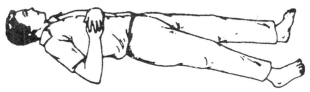

Practice of abdominal (or diaphragmatic) breathing for relaxation. In inhalation, abdomen goes up and during exhalation, abdomen goes down.

By consciously restoring our breathing to a pattern of relaxed state and also by various special breathing exercises (called as '*pranayama* techniques'), we eliminate the imbalances in body and mind and thereby achieve relaxation.

Laughter: A good laughter decongests the brain and thoroughly relaxes facial muscles. It also relaxes partially the other muscles of the body because in a good laughter the whole body vibrates.

73

Diet, Nutrition, and Elimination of Toxins: Although not given much importance, they play a crucial role in our stress levels. As it is already explained, certain types of food directly activate our stress mechanism. Similarly wrong habits of eating, e.g. overeating, eating at irregular intervals, eating wrong combination of food, etc. have a subtle influence in creating imbalance in our system which results in stress. Similarly if waste products and toxins generated in the body are not properly eliminated, they create an imbalance and generate stress. By fasting occasionally and resorting to other methods for elimination of toxins like steambath, enema, purification techniques described in *hatha yoga* (*kunjal, neti, tratak, kapalbhati* etc.), we can reduce such imbalance. In fact various techniques described earlier like massage, accupressure, exercises, breathing all help in effective disposal of toxins from the body.

Dancing and Shaking of the Body: Dancing helps in relaxing the body in the same way as aerobic exercises do. Shaking of various limbs of the body quickly and with jerks also removes tension in them and loosens them.

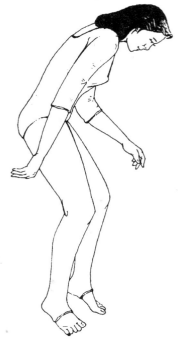

74

Rocking and Swinging : Get into a rocking chair and rock to and fro. It reduces tension. Similarly swinging to and fro in a *jhoola* also reduces tension. These activities actually produce a sensation of lightness creating a feeling of mental euphoria which relaxes the body and mind.

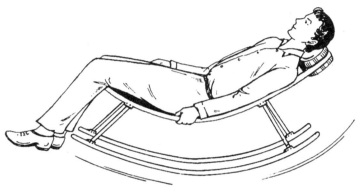

Music: Music has a great power in soothing a tired and tense mind. A distracted mind easily becomes centred on the pleasant music and songs. In fact nowadays *'music therapy'* has emerged as a separate branch of therapy in which different types of music are tried for curing various physical and psychological disorders. However, classical music, old melodious songs, devotional music and Bhajans have been found to be generally soothing for a restless and disturbed mind.

Soothing Touch of 'Nature': Whenever you get tense, go close to nature like gardens, forests, mountains, rivers, lakes etc. See the open sky, clouds and inhale fresh air.

Listen to chirping of birds, sound of moving breeze. Take healing rays of sun on your body. Play with children in open fields.

□ □ □

> *Note*: As such Mind, Thoughts & Stress are not independent things. They are functionally interrelated. Only for the purpose of explanation, they have been categorised as separate chapters in this book.

4

Mind Elevating Articles

MEANING AND PURPOSE OF LIFE

Some people spend their life as if they have to somehow pass the time of their life by indulging in whatever work comes their way. They mindlessly run here and there without understanding the larger aim of life which underlies all our activities. They take up something, but after a while become tired of it and then take up another thing. Many of us go through life in a similar way. We wander about aimlessly in one direction or other, seeking as many adventures as possible. But after travelling through the uncountable variety of lands, homes, jobs, encounters, relationships and projects that life has to offer, we remain puzzled as to what it was all about. All too often in this journey of life we come to the end looking back and wondering as to what was the purpose of all this running about.

We believe that by accumulating a lot of such experiences, we increase our awareness and consciousness but in reality the process is just the opposite. *It is only by giving up and letting go that the consciousness expands. The expansion of consciousness doesn't lie in the quantitative accumulation of experiences but in a qualitative change in one's consciousness.*

The reason for this aimless approach to life is that the consciousness of most human beings is not fully developed. Their consciousness usually have a limited range and focus due to which they are not able to see the things in their entirety. It (their consciousness) can be compared to a small light which illuminates only small portions here and there, but never knowing the full design and the meaning and purpose of what is being touched. In other words most human beings have only a partial awakening of their consciousness.

The growth of consciousness doesn't consist in travelling with a small and uncertain light that illuminates only small segments of the vast unknown. It is the systematic expansion of one's consciousness to the extent that everything can be understood and appreciated in its entirety in relation to the whole and there remain no scope for partial and distorted truth.

The underlying goal of our life is to attain this highest state of consciousness where consciousness is fully expanded and developed. In this state our identity is not narrowly confined but embraces all. Everything can now be known and understood properly in its true and unbiased state. *In the process of growth, this underlying purpose of our lives should remain stable despite all the changes we undergo in life. This is what provides the meaning and purpose to our life.*

One of the major changes which occurs when consciousness expands is a movement from self centeredness to selflessness. When the light of consciousness is small, whatever is not included in its boundaries is alien to it. Thus an individual whose consciousness is not well developed will be unable to appreciate the concerns and viewpoints of others. There will be considerable conflict in this person's life in relation to his environment. But as consciousness expands we become less self-centered and less preoccupied with trivial individual concerns.

As consciousness gradually expands, we keep on climbing to a higher vantage point from where we can see things from a larger perspective which allows us to be less concerned and anxious and enable us to see things as they really are and not as we imagined about them from a narrow perspective. One's thinking, feeling, attitudes and self concept are systematically transformed as consciousness is expanded. The world and the people remain the same but our angle of vision towards them changes totally.

When consciousness remains at a low level, one's identity remains totally confined and narrow. One's life is always occupied with 'I', 'me', 'mine'. This creates for us a sense of separation from all that we define as 'not I'. And this separation creates discomfort, disharmony and at times a feeling of loneliness and isolation. The experience of separateness arouses anxiety. It is indeed the source of all anxiety. The more narrow is one's concept of identity, the more insecure he will be, feeling small in the world which seems large and threatening. He looks himself as an isolated being struggling against the rest of the world. Such a person works primarily to achieve security and his chief concern is self protection.

Yoga and spirituality helps us transcend constricting identities to achieve a more encompassing awareness of who and what we are and finally establish ourselves in our true nature which is full of peace, happiness and bliss. Expanded identity involves less self preoccupation and more concern for others. When this happens, even in a minor way, there is a feeling of openness and lightness. We come to a greater awareness of the way in which all beings are interrelated. Our sense of separation between ourselves and others become less and less acute. We organize our lives to work for the common benefit, or all of us rather than for me and mine.

A person with a narrow identity can't see a larger pattern of his life. In giving he feels that some part of him is being lost. But the person with an expanded identity views himself as intimately connected with the whole. Instead of acting from a sense of isolation and insecurity, he begins to act from a sense of fullness and interrelatedness. *The idea of working and living only for himself seems quite absurd to him.*

If we wish to grow, all the identifications in terms of 'me' and 'mine' must slowly be abandoned and replaced. These identifications lead to conflict and unhappiness. Although each of the things in the world apparently has a separate identity, yet when we go to the very source, we find that there is an underlying unity in the apparent diversity. *The aim of all Yoga and spirituality is a movement from separateness to unity.*

PLEASURES AND PAINS OF LIFE

Life of a normal person is spent in constantly pushing pains and attracting pleasures. He attempts to repeat pleasurable experiences and becomes addicted to those objects, people and situations that have given him pleasure. He fiercely tries to hold on to them simultaneously avoiding all that is unpleasant and goes through all the stress that is involved in the process. For example when he does not succeed in getting the objects of pleasure, he falls into an emotional turmoil creating agitation in

80

mind. Sometimes in his madness for seeking pleasure and avoiding pain, he ignores the needs and concerns of others and thus creates a conflict in his relationships. Sometimes in the pursuit of pleasure he acts in a way which he knows is against his conscience and better judgement. Thus he creates internal conflicts also. Thus a person revolving in the wheel of pleasure and pain having attraction to pleasure and aversion to pain, inevitably and constantly remains under stress and realizes at the end of his life that it was all a futile race he was running althrough and he has wasted his whole life in these vain pursuits.

Characteristics of Pleasure and Pain

It should be noted that by the word 'Pleasure' in this chapter we are referring to *Rajasik* and *Tamsik* pleasures and not the *Satwik* pleasures. For example, when you enjoy a natural scenery, it is also a pleasure but it is *satwik* pleasure and is not harmful for you. Similarly, when you relish a melodious song or 'Bhajan', it gives you *satwik* pleasure which is beneficial for you.

To be able to separate oneself from the clutches of pleasure and pain, first it is essential to understand the nature and philosophy of pleasures and pains which we frequently come across in this changing world of names and forms. Following points make a humble attempt in this direction.

Pleasure and Pain Are Inseparable from Each Other:
Pleasure and pain are twins. They are two faces of the same coin. Where one is there the other is also bound to be present. This is inbuilt in the nature of worldly things that pleasures obtained by them are mixed with pain. No great illustrations are required to prove this. We are experiencing it daily in our day to day life.

Pleasure and Pain Are Transitory in Nature: This means that neither pleasure nor pain is permanent. They are fleeting, everchanging and shifting. Pleasurable objects and experiences can't remain permanently with us and in the same state. This is because of the everchanging nature of the world where nothing remains static. If everything changes and perishes in due course, then how the pleasures and pains obtained by them can remain permanent. They provide only momentary thrill till you are in contact with them.

Worldly pleasures can give only momentary joy

Pleasure Ceases to Be Pleasure After Sometimes: It is a common experience of our life that the same thing cannot give pleasure for a long time. For example suppose you are very anxious to eat some sweets. For sometime you will relish this experience very much. But a stage will come when you wouldn't want it any more and if it is given forcefully, you will rather feel repulsion and vomit. To quote another example, suppose you are very excited and keen to visit some place. Initially, you will enjoy the experience and obtain great pleasure but a stage will come when you start feeling bored to

82

remain at that place. You would like to return from there. So this is with all pleasures. They are short-lived and satisfy only temporarily and turn into boredom or dryness after sometime. In other words, we can say *that every experience of pleasure has a peak beyond which it no more remains a pleasure.*

The More Pleasure You Get, the More You Want: This is another nature of worldly pleasures that the temporary enjoyment you get from these pleasures, makes you more restless and desperate to repeat those pleasurable experiences again and again. The more you repeat the experience, the more your desperation to repeat it further grows on and on until you are totally taken over and destroyed by them. *Pleasure never satisfies a person, it only leads to a more desperate search for pleasure. It is like an itch that increases when scratched, like a fire that increases as more fuel is poured on it.* In fact attachment to pleasure is like an addiction where we constantly seek higher and higher levels of pleasure to satisfy our needs.

Endless Race in Running After Objects of Pleasure: After you get bored from an object of pleasure after some time, the matter does not end here. You do not remain silent after that. Then you start searching for another object of pleasure. Mind constantly wants to be tickled by a variety of pleasing sensations. To quote an example, suppose you are desiring to eat an ice cream cone. After your desire of eating ice cream cone is fulfilled you get a momentary satisfaction. But soon after this your mind will begin to search for another object of pleasure. You start thinking, what should I do now? May be I should go to a movie." You fulfil this desire and again a momentary satisfaction is realized, only to make you dissatisfied again and seek something new.

In this way your mind is kept constantly busy and restless and your whole life is consumed in the process of pursuing one satisfaction after another. *You find little islands of enjoyment in the midst of preponderance of restlessness.*

Pleasure Is in the Mind, Not in the Objects: Mind plays a vital role in the enjoyment of pleasures. It is in the mind where we feel pleasure. Objects play a secondary role. Suppose while enjoying a pleasure you hear some sad news, or some horrible thought of fear arises in your mind suddenly, then the same pleasure immediately loses all its charm. Similarly if your mood is not well then you can't enjoy a pleasure in the same manner. In a similar way, pains by various worldly objects and events are essentially felt in mind. Depending upon how you react to them and whether you take them lightly or seriously, you can diminish or increase the pain in your mind.

More Time Is Spent in Pursuing After Pleasures Than in Actually Enjoying Them: It is a general experience that a person running after pleasures, spends most of his time in pursuing them and has little time to enjoy them. He lives in a state of uneasiness and unrest and loses so much energy in the pursuit of pleasures that even when he gets the objects of pleasure, he is not able to enjoy it fully. If after pursuing, he does not acquire the object of his pleasure, you can easily think about his mental state. In short, more time and energy is spent in running after the pleasures rather than enjoying them.

Actual Pleasure Is Always Less Than The Imagined Pleasure: It is our general experience that actual pleasure obtained by us by contact with an object, person, place or a situation is always less than what we had imagined. Imagination always projects things in exaggerated and magnified form, different from the reality.

Amount of Pain Coupled with Pleasure Is Much More Than The Pleasure Initially Enjoyed: Although as we have mentioned earlier, every pleasure is mixed with pain yet if you examine carefully you will realize that the quantum of pain associated with pleasures is much more than the amount of pleasure associated with them. Some amount of pain you have to suffer initially in the efforts of pursuing the object of pleasure and some pain you suffer after the pleasing experience is over as its consequence.

For example suppose you are desiring to have some spicy food or snacks to satisfy the craving of your tongue. Now initially you will have to undergo the pain of going upto the required shop. Then you will have to wait there in the queue till your number comes. You may also have a fight there with the waiter or any other person for not cooperating in the matter of giving you the food at the right time and in the right manner or not giving you a proper seat. After the food comes, you may find that some article of food is not well prepared. Any way you finally eat the food and after having that momentary pleasure, the later consequences will be that spicy and oily food may have some adverse effect on your health. Your stomach may go unwell, you may have indigestion, heart burning and nausea etc. Another pain you may suffer is the mental urge and impulse to repeat that pleasurable experience of eating again.

To quote another example, suppose you are attached to a person and want to live with him. Now even after you manage to live with him/her, you also come across many other facets of his behaviour/habits which pinch you and you have to bear with them. Further when such a person leaves your company after some time due to any unavoidable circumstances or even leaves you for the time

85

being, you suffer further mental agony of his/her separation.

Then How Can You Find Real Happiness?

From the above discussion, you will be absolutely clear that no permanent satisfaction can be found in pleasures of the world. *They can only increase the restlessness and agitation of one's mind. Then how to attain real happiness and peace of mind?*

Real happiness does not reside in the objects but in the state of mind which is independent of these objects. It (true happiness) is an intrinsic property of our inner self and can be tapped if we learn to turn our attention from the external world to the inner world (our true self) off and on by meditation. Most people feel that without objects to strive after, we would be in a state of emptiness or boredom. This misconception is based upon viewing objects as the source of gratification in the world. *They do not have the realization that joy can be experienced without objects. Real source of joy, peace and happiness is within us and we do not have to run after anyone or anywhere to get it.*

However, it does not mean that we should abandon the world or hate material objects. Material objects, themselves, are not the problem, it is our attachment towards them which creates problem. Yoga encourages a healthy attitude towards material objects. We are encouraged to enjoy the experience and to utilize material objects to accomplish our goals, but should avoid becoming attached to them. We should use them as our servants and not allow them to become our masters and dominate us.

Once we develop detachment and dispassion towards worldly objects and events, then pleasure and pain automatically lose hold on us. We are released from the tight rein of pleasure and pain. We develop a deep attitude of equanimity towards all pleasures and pains and remain equiposed in most adverse circumstances, neither elated by gains, nor depressed by losses. *No worldly situation can disturb our inner peace and balance.* Gita also says, *'For the pleasures that come from the world, bear in them sorrows to come. They come and go, they are transient, not in them do the wise rejoice.'* In fact wise men never seek for sensual pleasures deliberately and thus remain freed from the pains associated with them because pain exists only when there is pleasure. So there is a very simple formula that if you don't want pains, avoid running after pleasures also.

Hence rather than becoming attached to the sensation of pleasure and trying to hold on to it while pushing pain away, simply witness them like a detached observer and take note of their coming and passing with full control on your mind.

PROBLEMS AND LIMITATIONS IN LIFE

Problems Are an Integral Part of Life

Problems are an integral part of life. They will never end. One problem goes, another comes. This is a natural cyclic process in life. Life is designed like this that you will face certain problems and learn the needed lessons to grow further. This is not only with you, it is with everybody. Nobody is without problems.

It is very immature for someone to think or imagine that his life should be very comfortable and free of any problem. Take it for granted that *there will always be ups and downs and unexpected things in life. You have to be prepared or anything.* Such is the natural law of life. Infact if a person's life is devoid of any problems or chal-

Problems will continue to keep coming in your life

lenges, he may be bored to death. So, we should learn to live with problems gracefully. If we can learn to welcome problems, they will eventually loose their 'Hold' upon us and we will become their master instead of slave.

Problems Come to Teach Us Certain Lessons: They Are for Our Ultimate Good

Regarding various problems, pains and discomforts which we face in life, try to develop the philosophy that these have not come to frighten us. Don't view these problems as burdens coming to us suddenly out of nowhere. They have come to us as per certain law. There is nothing in this world which happens by chance or accident. There is a reason for everything which happens to you. You are bound by a great relationship of cause and effect. For every effect there is a cause and for every cause there is an effect.

In fact these pains and discomforts are the very things we need to strengthen us and grow wherever we are lacking. They are the trying times for us and instead of getting puzzled by them, we should stop for a while, do some self evaluation and introspection and learn the needed lessons from them. *We can derive some benefit and lessons from every problem/difficulty of life and exploit it to our advantage. This is a wonderful law of life.*

If we oppose these discomforts and accuse ourselves and others, we are simply invoking a new chain of cause and effect and making matter worse. Remember that *everything which happens to us in life is for our good only. In the apparently looking cruel and adverse circumstances is hidden the infinite mercy of God* which we can realize if we properly contemplate upon it.

Infact you should consider all problems as projects and new opportunities instead of hindrances. Tackle them as you work for a new project or new assignment step by step instead of treating them as something foreign or external to you. Sooner you accept them as a part and parcel of different phases of your life, the better it is as they will become your servants and helpers instead of trouble makers and then only you will be at peace with yourself.

As you learn many lessons of life, problems in your life will also be proportionately reduced and your life will be comparatively smoother as you see with some saintly persons.

Problems Come alongwith Their Solutions

It is a general experience of life that when problems come to us, their solutions also come alongwith. This is because problems are not caused to us by the Almighty to harass us or frighten us or punish us. The purpose of problems is to bring out those virtues and finer aspects in us which are still dormant and haven't been awakened and to eliminate the undesirable traits from our personality.

89

We are never given a burden which we can't bear. If you look back upon your life you will surely find that although you encountered many problems, still you could always find some solution or the other. It was rare that you got stuck to a problem for ever and couldn't go beyond it. Knowing these truths and the benevolence of God behind allotting the problems to us we should never lose courage and get demoralized by problems. Rather we should face them with full confidence that we can definitely overcome them no matter how grave they are.

No Problem Is Permanent

We should also realize that no problem or difficulty confronting us is permanent. They all will pass. Nothing remains static in this world. Everything is in a state of constant flux and motion. Such is the law. Darkness is always followed by light. There can never remain the same condition always. Even the darkest days of your life will surely pass. This is inbuilt in the nature of life. Realizing this, a person should never become pessimistic and low in spirit in the face of problems.

Don't run away from problems. Face them boldly. Running away is not a way to be free from them. They will stick to you more tightly if you try to evade them. *Have a headlong collision with them and shatter them to pieces.*

No Problem Is Greater Than You

Remember there is no problem in the world which is greater than your strength and which can't be solved. Everything can be accepted and handled with serenity. There is nothing which can be called a catastrophe. Hence you should treat the problems and control them like your servant and never allow them to become your master. All forces of nature and circumstances must bow down before a calm and serene mind. If we also remain connected to God and seek His help, solutions of our problems can be found much quicker. God is ever available to help us provided we ask for it and join our hands in His hands.

We Should Thank God Even During Problems and Difficulties

You should also realize that compared to the comforts given to us by God, these problems are nothing. While enjoying comforts and luxuries of life, we are neither thanking God nor questioning why these luxuries have been given to us. But in pains and problems, we are so much perturbed. Is it not a fallacy? If we start doing the former, the HOLD of the latter will automatically reduce. *Infact we should adopt thanks-giving attitude to God not only for the comforts and luxuries provided to us* but also for the problems and difficulties because these are also meant for our ultimate good.

Don't Surrender Before the Limitations of Life

You may have certain limitations in your life which are blocking your way to progress although you wish to progress. Please note that all these limitations are with you according to the law of Karma or the law of destiny. No one is to blame for this except you yourself because of your past actions. So *there is no point in cursing yourself or God or others.*

It is also true that many of these limitations can't be removed by you overnight, i.e. you will have to live with them. *But remember in whatever conditions/limitations you are, you can always make some changes. These changes will pave the way for bigger changes.* All the doors are never closed for anyone. *Everyone is given a chance to grow further and to come out of the vicious circle of law of Karma however bad a person may have been. No one is doomed to eternal hell.*

So by your efforts, determination and applying the power of your free will, you can gradually frustrate the forces of your destiny and be above your destiny. *Reaching at this stage, your destiny doesn't move you but you decide your destiny and the course of action of your life. By your efforts, will and determination you can not only modify your destiny but even frustrate it fully.* If you have a strong desire and will, and working for a right cause, there is no force on earth or heaven which can prevent your success. All the forces of the Universe must support your mission.

You have been placed by God exactly where you deserve. This placing is actually needed by you for your growth or for working out/balancing some *karmas. Once you play your present role successfully, you will be automatically shifted to the next higher role.*

Continue to Progress Even During Problems

Some people think that when all of their problems will be over, they will then start their development plans of life. But the tragedy is that problems will keep on creeping in till the end of life. But this doesn't mean that you won't make any progress in life.

Let problems not interfere in the process of your development. In whatever miserable state you may be, go on developing yourself in whatever fronts you can because whatever be your problems, some avenues always remain open for further growth. It never happens that you can't do anything. *If fate closes one door for you, it also opens another door.*

92

Don't Imagine Problems, Just Face Them as They Come

Some persons waste a lot of their time in imagining many future problems for them, i.e. lest this or that should happen to them. In this connection please remember that problems and adverse happenings in life should be just faced as and when they come. One should not constantly dwell and focus on possible future mishappenings which may fall upon him. For example, don't think that what will happen if I get cancer, what will happen if my children leave me alone in old age or what will happen if I lose my job and so on. Infact you will find that ninety nine percent of things you imagine never take place. They are just creations of your doubtful mind and wild imagination.

As I have earlier mentioned that even if some mishappenings happen to you, you always have the power to handle them. *No problems and mishappenings can be greater than you.* Further you are never left alone in any adversity. Omniscient and Almighty God is always with you in whatever situation you may be. The whole world may forsake you but he won't. So never lose heart and always remember this principle *'Just face the problems. Don't dwell and brood over them.'*

Cope with One Problem at a Time

We all are surrounded by umpteen number of problems. If we start thinking and tackling all the problems at the same time, we will become mad and won't be able to solve even one problem properly. The correct approach is that you make a list of all your problems and then first pick up one problem on priority basis and concentrate on that problem only at a time. Shut out all other problems temporarily. By coping with one problem at a time, you will find the problem not overwhelming but stimulating. You will enjoy the adventure of problem-solving. It is only when you look at and try to solve all the problems simultaneously that you get overwhelmed by them.

93

NATURE AND CONTROL OF DESIRES

It is said that man is a bundle of desires and it is these unlimited desires which keep him constantly agitated and mobile. The number of desires of a single person can be as many as the number of stars in the universe. No man on this earth has ever been able to satisfy all his desires. It is said that even if a man be handed over all the possessions of the world and all the objects of pleasures, still he will not be satisfied and will desire more of them. Therefore a man with desires in his mind has never died peacefully. *Unfulfilled desires keep the mind agitated and restless even after death and become the cause of his next birth.*

However, it should be clear that by the word 'desires' in this chapter, we are signifying to 'lower desires' or 'ego based desires' as listed later in this chapter. There are 'higher desires' also in human beings e.g. desire to know the meaning and purpose of life, desire to know about soul, God and universe; desire for your spiritual growth and attainment of everlasting joy, peace, bliss, freedom; desire to do something creative and constructive for the society etc. There is nothing wrong in pursuing these higher desires.

Similarly, pursuing your basic needs for survival & comfort within a reasonable amount (e.g. food, shelter, clothing, sex, self-protection etc.) also don't come under the word 'desire'. We can also say that lower desire belong to ego while higher desires belong to our soul or spirit and basic survival needs belong to our lower or instinctive mind (as in animals).

Classification of Desires

Desires can be broadly classified as follows:

• Desire for (Rajasik & Tamasik) sensual pleasures.

• Desire for acquisition and storage of more and more wealth, property, money.

• Desire based on insecurities and fears e.g. taking excessive physical safety measures, collecting more & more friends, relatives, children, making many social and political connections to make up the feeling of insecurity, inadequacy, loneliness and boredom.

- Desire for more and more physical and material comforts and luxuries.
- Desire for attainment of name, fame, status, power, appreciation etc.

Nature and Characteristics of Desires

To overcome the desires, it is first necessary to understand their basic nature and characteristics. Some of their important features are described below:

Desires Are Endless. Nobody Can Satisfy All His Desires: No matter how hard you try, you can never satisfy all your desires. This is because desires of every person are unlimited. Everybody wants everything. Hence by sheer logic it is impossible for anyone to fulfil all his desires.

Desires are never ending

Desires Multiply Faster Than You Can Satisfy Them:
According to Swami Vivekananda *if your power to satisfy desires increases in Arithmetic progression, the power of desires increases in geometric progression.*

If you satisfy one desire, it gives rise to ten more desires, why? Because the root cause of desires is your illusion that happiness can be achieved by outer material things of the world. But in reality *no outer object or condition can give you that eternal happiness which you are seeking at the core of your heart. This is because no object or condition of the world is perfect. Everything has some shortcoming or the other and has a scope for further improvement.* So when you don't get this happiness by one thing, you think you may get it by another thing. In this way you go on pursuing one thing after another in a vain attempt to get this happiness and that's how your desires are fanned.

Another reason of fanning of your desires is that you always want more and more, better and better, no matter whatever you have got. This is again due to the fact that nothing is absolute and perfect in this world. Everything is relative and dual. But, in ignorance, we assume that by getting more of the same thing or by getting a better thing compared to the present thing, we may be satisfied. This is where the trap lies. *And in this world whatever you may get, there are always better things available than the things you possess.* If they don't exist today they will appear tomorrow. So as soon as you come across these better things (which you are bound to come across sooner or later) you again become restless to get these better things. This is how your desires are fanned.

Further in today's world man's exposure and mobility are constantly increasing because of which invariably he comes across better and better things which act as a fuel in fanning his desires. For example suppose you fulfil your desire for purchasing a car somehow and you become the owner of a car. Now after sometime you see a car with more facilities and better looks, so you develop a desire to buy that car. This is how this vicious circle goes on endlessly. Similarly to quote another example, suppose you had desired appointment for a certain post and you got your desire fulfilled. Now you see some other person at a higher post than you, enjoying higher privileges and power. Again a desire is born in you to achieve that post and so on.

So the conclusion is that *the possession of the desired object only feeds or ignites the desire further instead of quenching it* because it makes the mind more and more susceptible to search for greater comforts and greater attraction. By yielding to one desire, we increase the power of other desires to attack us easily. It is as if we have let loose the string by submitting to one desire.

Needs Can Be Fulfilled but Not Desires: As far as a man's basic needs are concerned they are limited and can be fulfilled. Needs are related to a man's effective survival in the world and these are necessary to be met.

But the desires of even a single person can't be fulfilled because the basis of desires is greed which can never be satisfied. It always wants more and more, better and better no matter how much you feed to it and since this world can constantly produce better and better things in material sphere, the stage is set for constant running after objects of desire.

Desires Are Preceded and Succeeded by Anxieties : Whenever man has a desire, he becomes anxious as to how he can get the object of his desire. He goes through

97

all stress and strains to grab the object of his desire. The great anxiety preceding the acquisition of the desired object can't be regarded as a state of happiness or satisfaction.

Whenever the desired object is obtained, there is again an anxiety and fear of losing the object. Things are made in such a way that they can be taken away from us by natural causes or other factors of life. There is a possibility of deprivation of the acquired object even after one's having it after so much hard labour. So this is another form of anxiety as to how to keep the acquired thing safe and intact.

Hence there is a preceding anxiety and also a succeeding anxiety which can never be called akin to happiness or satisfaction. So you can see that one's desire is like a disturbance in the calm lake of mind.

Happiness Obtained by Fulfilment of Desires Is Momentary and Illusory: There is of course a momentary happiness alongwith satisfaction after the object of desire has been obtained. But if you reflect deeply, you will find that even the source of this momentary satisfaction is not the object but something else.

What happens is that after the possession of the desired object, mind which was earlier moving towards the object, becomes still and returns to its original calm state. The cessation of desire tentatively brought about by the acquisition of the object, is the cause of happiness and not the object.

But notice that this stillness of mind obtained is only temporary because you can't remain in this state for long and soon you are engulfed with the succeeding anxiety associated with the desired object as explained earlier.

Happiness is Neither Fulfilment nor Repression of Desires. It Is Cessation of Desires: We have mentioned above that desire is like a disturbance in the calm mental state. Considering this there are some people who don't fulfil their desires but repress them. So root of the desires still remains in the mind although they are not outwardly expressed. This repression of desires may lead to various psychological and physical disorders in the person. You may ask if both, expression as well as repression of desires, lead to disturbances, then what is the solution? *Disturbance created by desires can neither be eliminated by fulfilling the desires nor by repression of desires but only by cessation and giving up of desires. This gives you the key to happiness.*

It is to be noted here that our lower mind or lower nature is very turbulent and it doesn't easily give up its tendency of desiring one thing after another. It desires one thing and gets momentarily satisfied by fulfilling it, then desires another thing and again gets momentarily satisfied only to be dissatisfied again for pursuing further desires. Your lower mind can't stick to one thing for a long time. It always wants varieties. It gets bored with one thing after sometime and then seeks another thing for its satisfaction. Consequently it remains in preponderance of restlessness amidst momentary satisfaction. If left to its own, it will create chaos and hell in your life by becoming a demon of desires. To prevent this aimless wandering of mind in countless desires and temptations, one should always channel his mind towards some constructive activities. An undirected mind without a goal always turns towards destructive activities.

THE ART OF RELAXED AND EFFICIENT WORKING

Everybody in this world is doing some work or the other. No body can remain without doing any work. It is the natural instinct of soul to remain engaged in some kind of work. That is why this Earth or World is sometimes referred to as *karma-kshetra* (Field of Action). However there are many people who while working remain constantly tense and agitated. But there are also few wise people who inspite of working hard, enjoy their work. Infact work is a source of joy and happiness for them.

There is an art of doing action called *Karma Yoga* in yogic parlance by which you can do your work most skillfully, efficiently while remaining cheerful and stress-free. Infact work becomes a means for the upliftment and happiness of such a person.

The salient features of this art of skilful action are described below.

Attention & Awareness

This is the first ingredient of 'Karma Yoga' in which whatever you do, your attention and awareness should be totally focussed on that. No matter how trivial, routine or habitual an activity is but your awareness shouldn't drift from that activity. For example, suppose you are washing your utensils, you should be completely absorbed in that task, oblivious of anything else in the world. This should be the most important activity for you in the world at that time. You should be fully aware of each and every step involved in washing the utensils. Not a single step should go unnoticed or be done absentmindedly, i.e. the activity shouldn't become mechanical and automatic devoid of your conscious attention. This is the meaning of undivided attention and awareness.

100

This thing in other words is also called present centeredness or remaining in the present moment. Normally it is seen that when a person does any habitual activity like driving a car, taking a bath, eating the food, his mind easily drifts from the activity of the present moment. His mind will drift either to past or future or some other activities going on in the vicinity. But this is exactly what is to be avoided. By exercise of your will power you have to bring the mind to the activity in your hand. This eventually increases the strength and control over your mind. Drifting or straying of mind too frequently from the task in hand is a sign of weak mind.

When you learn to pay attention to each and every small activity you are doing, you will not only be able to do that activity in the best manner, but you will also feel a sense of inner joy in your mind. Day-to-day mundane and routine activities will become quite interesting and a source of great satisfaction for you. With this attitude you can enjoy each and every moment of your life. *Happiness doesn't come from the work we are doing but by our attitude associated with the work and our ability to remain fully immersed in the work.*

Any work done with attention and awareness becomes a source of joy

101

Detachment

After doing any activity with one pointed awareness and undivided attention, you should also be able to forget this activity completely after the job is over without any thoughts about the old activity lingering in your mind. You should now be fresh and wide awake for the next activity or work in hand and while taking on to the next activity, there shouldn't be any thought of the tasks completed or yet to be done. Once again the attention is focussed only on the new task right now in the hand.

This also means, in other words, that one shouldn't get attached to any work one is involved inspite of doing it sincerely and with dedication. Alongwith concentration you have to develop the ability to detach from a task and attend to another task at a moment's notice and this is what Swami Vivekananda also stressed. He was of the opinion that faculties of concentration and detachment should be developed simultaneously. Purpose of all work should be growth of the mind and not that we become attached and bound by it.

Elimination of Doership Feeling

Eliminate the feeling of 'I-ness', 'me', 'mine' while doing work, e.g. 'I am doing' or 'I have done' or 'only I can do', etc. *The harsh truth is that in reality you can't do any thing on your own. Controller of the world is a much superior power than me and you.* If you reflect deeply, you will readily understand as to why it is true that you are not the doer as explained in the next paragraph.

There are so many uncertainties and other factors (natural as well as man-made) involved in execution of a thing that it is impossible to associate your proprietorship in doing a thing. Many of such factors are beyond your control. The truth is that you can achieve a thing only if supported or cooperated by God. So in the final analysis it is God who does every thing and not you. You simply act as a physical instrument.

Hence eliminate ego and doership feeling while doing work. Have the feeling that you are only acting as a faithful servant of God or as a Divine instrument. *This shift of your attitude from 'Doer to Divine'* will bring about a considerable change in the quality of your mind and quality of your work. Your ego will be completely erased leading to purity of mind. Ego is the greatest hindrance in the spiritual progress of a man and the above shift in attitude gradually puts an end to this great barrier clearing your way for your onward journey towards the ultimate truth and reality.

This shift in attitude from 'Doer to Divine' converts all your ordinary work into spiritual activities. The whole life becomes 'Yoga' for you. You don't have to search for a separate time for doing yoga or *Sadhana*. You are infact practicing 'Yoga in Action'. Quality of your work is automatically improved because there is no particular desire or expectation to distract your mind as results are totally left to God. Such a man even if rewarded after the work, doesn't take any credit for this and he humbly surrenders the reward to God. To quote an example, Hanuman, a highly reverred figure in the epic *Ramayana* had shown an exemplary courage in burning the whole Lanka. But he didn't accept the slightest credit for it and attributed his success totally to God.

Non-Expectation of Fruits

Some people often question that without any expectation of fruits what will be the motive power behind doing a work. Little do they realize that it is not the fruits or the results which gives you the joy, it is the consciousness or attitude associated with a work which gives you the joy. Infact any work can be made interesting to a supreme degree by paying attention to every bit of it and by trying to do it in the most systematic and best manner. It doesn't matter how insignificant or trivial a work is.

Hence the work done in the above spirit itself becomes a source of enjoyment. So you don't have to depend upon the fruits for getting enjoyment. You enjoy right in the work and the action itself becomes your reward.

Philosophy behind non-expectation of fruits also gains weight from the idea that fruits or results of any work whatsoever are not in our hand. This is the domain which is totally under God. Freedom is given to us only in the performance of action and not in the results. Final say in every matter is always of God and not of us. God, depending upon so many factors and merits of individual case, bestows the fruits of our efforts or actions. Hence there is no point in wasting time or breaking head over this aspect when it is none of our business. *Since God is perfect so we must be satisfied with whatever results He awards for our actions. Expectation of fruits is binding while renunciation of fruits is liberating.*

What Work to do

Now which work to do? Any work which is allotted to you as a part of your duty. The Yogic attitude to work is of absolute detachment, not to have any choice, but to accept and do whatever is given to you or whatever comes to you in your normal course of life. It is in that way and that way alone that all work becomes supremely interesting and all life a miracle. Man usually chooses his work or is made to choose a work because of a vital preference or prejudice or notion that it is the right kind of work in which he can shine or succeed. But this attachment or personal choice is more an impediment than a help towards finding the real joy of life.

Selfless Action

What is meant by doing work selflessly? It is to do a work because it is assigned to you as a duty and do it most attentively, skillfully, efficiently, systematically and as best as you can without any hope of personal gain. Whenever you do any good work (any work done selflessly for the larger welfare of mankind in the above mentioned spirit), you feel a peculiar inner joy. Any selfless work or service with the feeling of giving and helping others expands your consciousness and fills you with the inner contentment and bliss. *Bliss is never attainable by living a life of limited self interest.* On the other hand any work done selfishly contracts your consciousness and leads to bondage creating discomfort, disharmony and restlessness of mind.

Selfless service gives great joy

This inner joy and deepest sense of fulfilment obtained through selfless service is, the highest satisfaction achieved by a 'Karma Yogi' (man of selfless action). Swami Vivekananda has said, *'The end of all work is to*

105

bring out the essential divinity in man by selfless service. All work whether management, leadership, administration; all these have to be directed towards a single purpose—the manifestation of the essential divinity in man by working for good of others, good of millions, good of all beings'.

So in this way work is not something which you have to do just for earning your livelihood or as an obligation on others. When done in the right spirit, work becomes the instrument of growth, a way to self realization. Swami Vivekananda has beautifully explained in his book *Karma Yoga* that *paradoxically we don't need to do work for helping the world or to any person for that matter. World is self sufficient and will continue to operate for ever even without us. We require to do good work basically for helping ourselves because every good work done by us purifies us, elevates us and helps to bring out the hidden divinity in us.*

God is not depending on me and you for running or helping this world. We are simply given the opportunities to help others by God to improve ourselves. Otherwise all help is basically done by God only. We simply become the instruments of help because of our willingness to do so. Even if we are not willing to become the instrument, God has thousands of other means to provide help to somebody or something, if He so desires. Hence any egocentric feeling of helping others should be totally eliminated. Infact any help done by you should be forgotten as soon as possible.

Learn to Divide Your Work

All of us are always filled with many tasks to do, many problems to handle, many new plans to implement. But it is seen that ordinary man remains totally confused as to which work to start or do first. He spends most of the time thinking and planning and remains in utter confusion and turmoil devoting very less time for actual work.

The reason for this chaotic state of mind amidst work is that people try to think and do all the work at one time. The proper way to handle work is to first make a list of all the works in order of priority. Go on adding any new work in this list with priority status marked.

Now take out one work at a time from this list and at this stage forget all other works and get completely absorbed in this work as if this is the only task with you. Think not about the tasks just completed. Think not about the tasks yet to be done. Let them come to you in their own time without rushing at you all together. Once the task in hand is over, forget it completely like a closed file and take up the next task in queue. Now concentrate on this task, only on this task which you have taken right now in your hand.

This is the secret by which you can handle maximum work load with the least stress and confusion.

Avoid Aimless Work

Although *Karma Yoga* emphasizes non-expectation of fruits, but it doesn't mean that one shouldn't have any goals or aims while doing work. It only says that after you have decided the goals and done necessary planning to achieve these goals, put your whole mind in the process of work and not on the results. Infact aimless work is discouraged in Yoga.

Leading life aimlessly is like kicking a football in the field here and there without aiming it towards the goal of the other party. You must make some short-term and long-term goals in your professional as well as personal life and then systematically work towards them step by step. All these short term and long term goals will finally become the basis to attain the highest aim of life which is 'Self-Realization'. A directionless mind normally succumbs to its lower nature and becomes the victim of all types of vices and bestial instincts.

Consider All Work as God's Work

In Karma yoga, all works are considered as orders from the Divine no matter through whose medium they have come to you. No work is personal work in karma yoga. They are all God's works. Since a *karma yogi* considers himself as a servant of God, he does these works with complete sincerity and dedication and as best as he can so as to fulfil his true role as a servant of God and after completion, hands over these works to God in all humility. A *karmayogi* does intense work but leaves all results thereof to God.

DESTINY AND FREEWILL

From times immemorial, mankind has remained puzzled on the subject of Destiny and Free will. It has been one of the most difficult metaphysical riddles to solve. Some people think that their entire life is predetermined according to some destiny allotted to them by a whimsical God and they can't do anything about this and they are just puppets in the hands of fate. However there is another group which feels that everything in life depends upon one's self-efforts and destiny is nothing.

However the truth is that neither of these two groups is absolutely correct in their statements. Both are projecting only partial truth of the matter. The fact is that both destiny and free-will play their part in determining what happens in our life. They are two different forces and

108

the relative proportion of these two forces determine the ultimate result.

Fate or Destiny

Destiny is your rough life map and boundary conditions imposed by the Almighty on the basis of your past lives and actions, not with the intention of punishing you for the wrongful actions done by you but solely from the angle as to what kind of circumstances and conditions will benefit you most for your growth and further learning. Apparently some of the conditions in our life may appear cruel to us when seen casually but if we contemplate deeply we will find that in these apparently looking cruel and adverse circumstances is hidden the infinite mercy of God.

Free Will

Free will on the other hand is the limited freedom given to you for the performance of actions. Nobody's hands are totally chained in this world. Some freedom, either to a lesser degree or greater degree, has been given to everybody with the help of which he can make some changes and improvements in his life. These little changes pave the way for bigger changes leading to greater freedom. So by using your little freedom judiciously, a way is opened for your larger freedom. All the doors are never locked for any person however wicked he may be. Everybody is given a chance to improve. Nobody is doomed to eternal hell.

Interaction Between Free-Will and Fate

The concept of Free-will vis-a-vis Fate can be understood better by the following analogy. Suppose a cow is chained to a peg by a rope. Now the cow can't cross the circle formed by the rope (acting as a radius of the circle). This is called 'Fate'. But the cow has full freedom to walk inside the circle, this is called 'Free Will.' By observing the discipline and behaviour of the cow in her movement in the smaller circle, the cow owner may permit the cow to move in a larger circle gradually enhancing her freedom. A time may come when he can leave the cow totally free and unchained after observing the performance of the cow in the smaller freedoms given to her.

In this way we see that man is neither totally chained nor completely free. Looking back at the past, he is a slave of his destiny but looking at the future he is a producer according to his free will. *But seen with the totality of the vision, he has a limited freedom and limited bondage, relative strength of which vary depending upon how he has lived his life in the past and how he is living now.*

In fact, in real life incidents, the self-effort when exercised, mixes with the destiny to bring about a resultant effect in future. *So your past (or destiny) can be modified by the exercise of free-will in the present.* Your future is a continuity of the past modified in the present by your free-will. The freedom to modify the past and to create a future either for the better or worse is *purushartha* or 'self-effort'. Your self-effort combines with your past and makes your future better or worse. *So one can see that 'Destiny' is not something rigid. It is subject to constant correction and modification* depending upon the exercise of your limited freedom or free-will in the present.

Power of Free Will over Fate

Although Fate is a restricting force in life yet you can gradually defeat this force by using your Free Will or limited freedom granted to each individual judiciously. You needn't revolve helplessly like a slave in the wheel of destiny. You can detach yourself from this wheel by the application of your free-will and self efforts. *Destiny can never be greater than 'free will' because it itself is the creature of free will exercised by you in the past.* Your 'will' has the power to succeed in the end defeating all the forces of destiny. All the forces of destiny must bow down before a 'Determined will'. If you haven't been successful by applying some self efforts, you should increase your self efforts with redoubled vigour till you become victorious overpowering the forces of *prarabdha* (destiny). Hence the individual Free-will has the power to alter the destiny and even frustrate it fully.

Fate

Free will

Free will is stronger than fate

In fact, man has the power to increase his Free Will to such an extent that destiny can be totally frustrated. At this level he belongs to a plane where he is no more moved but can move the things and can change the inevitable circumstances and fixed conditions. So there is a higher power or higher plane which can override the lower plane of destiny of which the stars are the indicators.

This precisely is the aim of yoga to get out of the cycle of karma or destiny. By yoga you leave the mechanical process of nature in which you are an ignorant slave, a helpless and miserable tool in the hands of destiny. You rise into another plane where you become a conscious participant and dynamic agent in the creation or making of a higher destiny.

Animals Don't Have Freewill

This faculty of independent movement exists only in human beings. It is found lacking in animal and plant kingdoms. However as explained earlier even in case of human beings, its effect in life is modified by the play of destiny upon it. *Both destiny and Free Will act and react on each other. Both influence and are influenced by each other.*

Astrology & Fate

Neither *karma* nor astrology points to a rigid and immutable fate. Stars don't rule over our destiny. Stars merely record a destiny that has already been formed. They are only indicators and they often indicate several fate possibilities. Astrologers themselves say that there are two forces *daiva* and *purusartha*, i.e. 'fate' and 'individual energy' and the individual energy can modify and even frustrate fate. That's why there has never been a prophet who was infallible. Things are predictable in partonly because of the personal Free Will or endeavour associatedwith the destiny. There is no absolute rigidity in the plane of forces which decide destiny. It is often seen that when a person turns from the ordinary life to spiritual life, the predictions of the horoscope no more apply to that extent. Here it can be concluded that attainment of spiritual consciousness can easily annul the old destiny. Living on this plane or level

112

of consciousness one has more plastic freedom. When a person achieves the highest state of spiritual consciousness, he has unlimited freedom, not at all bound by destiny but he rather becomes the master of his/her destiny.

SOURCE OF REAL HAPPINESS

Attainment of happiness is the innate desire of every human being. Everything we do, we do for the sake of happiness. One gets married not for the sake of a wife or a husband, but for the sake of happiness. One seeks children for the sake of happiness. One pursues a job and earns money for the sake of happiness.

This is not surprising because seeking happiness is in our original nature. We will never feel satisfied until we achieve complete happiness—an absolute fulfillment that includes perfect peace, love, wisdom and joy. Our inner Self is filled with happiness, peace and love. The closer we go into the inner Self (or Real Self), the more happiness we experience.

But where do the humanity search for this happiness? In the things of the world, in possessions, in outer conditions, in relationships with other persons. *People are always seeking it in the wrong place, so they are constantly losing touch with it.* People are frantically searching but they can't find it at the place where they are looking for it and that leads to despair. And not just despair, tremendous resentment and anger accumulate in the process leading to a lot of violence sometimes.

Happiness lies inside and to attain it we need to turn within and travel toward our inner Self which is the fountain of infinite joy, peace and bliss and we can drink from it as much as we want. Yoga and meditation are the tools to carry out this inner journey towards our real Self.

113

Changeable & Perishable Things Can't Give Lasting Happiness

It is impossible to find this perfect and permanent happiness in anything or anyone or any condition in the world due to the very nature of creation. Everything in this creation is changeable and perishable and it is only logical to understand that impermanent and temporary things or situations can't give you lasting and permanent happiness. They can only give temporary illusory thrills and pleasures.

Another major reason why anything in the world can't give us true happiness is that creation is built on the principle of duality and relativity as explained in detail below.

Duality of the World

Definition of the world is that which is dual in nature meaning thereby that everything here is made of two opposite aspects, e.g. day-night, life-death, summer-winter, male-female, young-old, pleasure-pain, joy-sorrow, association-disassociation, etc.

These two aspects can't be separated from each other. They are inbuilt in the nature of worldly things. They are two faces of the same coin.

From this it is concluded that anything which gives you pleasure, also gives pain. Any person or thing which is associated with you must also dissociate or leave you at some time. If you have some gain or profit sometime, you may also suffer loss at some other time. If you have certain advantages from something, you will have certain disadvantages also. For example, when you marry you have certain pleasures and advantages but you have certain disadvantages too in the form of extra responsibilities, burdens and adjustments. Similarly when you buy a house somewhere, you have certain advantages but also certain anxieties and tensions associated with it. So this is with everything. Sometimes people see only one aspect of a thing and make their conclusion that it is very good or bad. But actually they forget to see the opposite aspect. This is why it is said that *what appears is not always the reality.*

The above is also called the Law of Divine Balance. So according to it, if you want to avoid pains and discomorts in your life, you will have to avoid pleasures and comforts also. *If you don't want insult you will have to give up the desire for praise also.* But the problem is that each of us would like to have just the good things—the pleasant and the beautiful but not the unpleasant and bad things. People believe that they can separate out all the suffering, pains and unpleasantness from the so called joys and pleasures of life. But this is impossible. This belief is one of man's biggest traps. In this dualistic world, there can't be pleasure without pain, light without darkness, good without evil. You can't have just one side of coin without the other. It comes down to the basic principle that *what we crave at the deepest level of our being can't be found in anything of the world.*

To find real happiness and bliss we will have to transcend this duality of the world. *The best way to remain unaffected by this dual nature of the world is to deal with worldly things and incidents with a detached outlook as if you are merely a spectator, i.e. neither get elated in success nor grieve in failure. Remain evenminded in gain/loss, success/failure, praise/insult. Once you reach to this mental level, you become free from the clutches of dualities.*

Relativity of the World

Third reason why worldly things don't satisfy you is that you always want something better no matter what you get because worldly things are all relative. Whatever you get, there are always better things available and you start looking towards them and in this way you always remain discontented and dissatisfied no matter what you get. *There is nothing absolute and perfect in the nature of world. Everything is superior or inferior only relatively.* For example, a rich person is superior to a beggar but inferior to a richer person.

Inter-dependence & Inter-connectivity of the world

Everything in this world is dependent on and connected to other things. Nothing is independent and stands in isolation with the rest of the world. There is an endless chain of inter-dependencies and inter-connectivities. So whatever you attain in this world is dependent and related to many things. So if those things or factors change, the status of attained thing will also undergo change and therefore the happiness based on your acquired thing can't be permanent.

Inner Self—The Source of Bliss

Everlasting happiness or bliss which is free from any opposite aspect comes from inside, the deep recesses of your inner self (soul). This is what we should strive to find through meditation and other practices of yoga.

As you become more aware of your inner self through yoga and meditation, you will automatically withdraw from dependence on objects and people as sources of gratification. This doesn't imply that you will no longer enjoy outside experiences. Infact you will enjoy this world more, being more free without any attachment or expectations from it. This only means that you will not depend on the world for your satisfaction, comfort and stability. *Your satisfaction and contentment will rest in yourself.* When you are dependent on people and objects for your pleasure, your whole vision gets coloured. *You are then not able to relate to them freely and enjoy.* Seeking happiness in the external world leads to small momentary islands of satisfaction in the midst of a preponderance of restlessness.

116

External Circumstances as Stressors

Many people have wrong beliefs and illusion that for their happiness, someone or something external to them should change. But often the people and situations around us can't be changed. We can not change and regulate this world because we are not the controller of this world. We can only change ourselves. So instead of putting more energy on changing outside circumstances and conditions, one should focus more on the inner changes in the mental attitudes and reactionary patterns based on right knowledge. It is not to say that one should never try to change his environment. To whatever extent possible one should definitely endeavour to improve his outside environment towards making it more positive, harmonious and congenial. But you should also learn to control your responses so that you are never disturbed no matter whatever happens to the outside world. *External events are never as important as our reactions towards them. However hard the external realities and facts may be, it is our attitude towards them which matters more.*

External problems, adverse conditions & circumstances only provide the material to disturb us but these are not the sole cause of our disturbance. They can create stress only if we add our negative reactions to them. In other words external events only act as a fuel which can catch fire only when it is ignited by the matchstick of mind. *So without support from our mind, no condition or circumstance can act as a stressor for us.*

SLOWING DOWN THE MIND

Mind of most of the people runs with a tremendous velocity with one thought after another. Their mind is not able to remain calm even for a moment. They are always planning, worrying, moving and tensing. Gradually it becomes a deep rooted habit and a type of mind set. Even when there is nothing to worry, these people search some cause for worry

117

and remain under free floating anxiety. When there is nothing to do, they move tense as to what to do now, instead of utilizing this opportunity to relax their minds.

What is meant by high velocity of mind? It is a parameter indicating the number of thoughts moving across your mind per unit of time. *Slowing down your mind essentially means reducing the number of thoughts* in your mind per unit of time. Suppose previously one thousand thoughts used to move across your mind in a minute, and now only hundred thoughts move in the same time. It means you have slowed down your mind to that extent. Mind velocity is particularly high during emotions of hurry, impatience and desperation.

High velocity of mind or the tremendous rush of thoughts in mind is essentially a sign of weak and uncontrolled mind. A controlled mind can continue to keep only one thought for as long as it desires without allowing other thoughts to come in. It may even remain thoughtless for a period of time it desires.

Now the way to reduce the velocity of mind is to slow it down to attend to only the present activity in your hand. Don't remain in the memory of past and anticipations and apprehensions of future. Learn to live in the present. *It is only when you think ahead of time and become past and future oriented that the speed of your mind increases* and it also leads to poor performance of the present task in hand.

Normally while doing anything, we think ahead of the time when this work will be finished and we can enjoy our leisure. In this process we neglect the present and spend our time in unhappiness. It is our future-oriented and rushing mind which blocks our happiness of the present moment and keeps our mind constantly agitated.

Once you learn to slow down your mind to the activity in hand, you will find that the most ordinary and mundane work, which used to be quite boring earlier, becomes quite interesting and a source of great joy and satisfaction.

118

It is only by slowing down and paying attention to each moment that many of the things happening around us which are normally taken for granted and seem dull and uninteresting, become highly interesting and enjoyable. If we want to experience joy and happiness in our work, we should leave the attitude of rushing through our activities and to somehow finish them as early as possible. This should be replaced by an attitude of care and awareness in each activity however trivial it may be. If we are not mindful in each small activity, we can't be mindful in carrying out important tasks also because attitude and frame of mind can't be suddenly changed.

LONELINESS AND BOREDOM

In spiritual parlance a lonely person is he who can't face himself and only such a person runs after other objects and people to keep his mind occupied. When he doesn't have any object or person to engage his mind, he feels bored. Boredom comes from wanting to have something but not having it. He doesn't realise that joy can also be experienced without objects by turning the attention within.

119

But depending on other persons and objects for your gratification is highly illusory because nothing is going to remain permanently with you in this world. Everything will leave you one day and then either by choice or by force you will have to live only with yourself. Even in our normal day to day busy life, moments come when we are alone and are only with ourselves.

If you can't live alone, it means you are not at peace with yourself. There are many conflicts and disturbances inside you which start troubling you as soon as you sit alone. So to avoid them you always want some external props in the form of objects and persons so that your mind may remain engrossed in outward things instead of your internal disturbances. But this is like running away and diverting yourself from the real problems. These stop gap arrangements won't give you the eternal peace and satisfaction which you are craving for at the core of your heart. They are like 'Labyrinth' *(Bhulbhullaia).*

Sooner or later you will have to come to terms with yourself or getting the peace you are craving for. *Running away from yourself is never the way to attain peace.* It only delays the attainment of peace. So the crux of the matter is that you have to learn to like yourself, to live with yourself. If there are any disturbing factors in your personality, try to resolve them rather than running away from them. Remember that finally it is only your own self which will live with you and not anything else in the world. At an advanced stage you should develop your mind frame to the extent that you may feel alone even while in the crowd and feel in the midst of people even while living alone.

We have all made it a habit to stay in a crowd. We are afraid of being alone, even though the reality is that our lonliness is our truth. We have come into the world alone, we are alone and we will depart alone. Is it not true that a person is always alone, even when surrounded by hundreds or thousands? Recognize your lonliness, know it and experience it. Everyday for a short time live as though you are alone in the world. At this time you are neither a husband, nor a wife, neither a father nor a son, neither an official nor a student, neither a man nor a woman. You are just you.

THE ART OF LETTING GO

Some people think that the way to one's development and happiness is to accumulate as many things as possible, encounter as many people and relationships in life as possible, change as many jobs as possible, travel as many places as possible etc.

But unfortunately these very people are the most dissatisfied lot. When they are exhausted with their life and look back, they wonder what was it all about. Why did they do all this running about?

121

Infact the truth is that happiness consists not in accumulating things but rather in giving up and letting go. The more you let go, the more relieved and relaxed you become. When you let go of everything, you become totally free. This *letting go* doesn't mean throwing and leaving everything you have. You may have everything and still you may be mentally detached from it. This is what is true *letting go*. This *letting go* is applied not only in case of material possessions and experiences but also in respect of various emotions rooted in your mind. For example, suppose you have some anxieties about certain things in your mind, some jealousy and hatred towards certain person; *just allow these feelings to drop like a stone falling in water and allow yourself to be free.*

There is a tense discomfort in clinging to something while there is a feeling of relief and relaxation in giving up the thing. *When you get attached or stuck to certain thing, freedom of your thought and action is lost* and you are likely to think and act in the world in terms of those attachments. Thereby you won't be able to see the reality as it is. This ignorance of reality creates discomfort and disharmony and stops your further growth in life.

DEATH OF EGO

In 'Spirituality', it is said that the death of ego is the emergence of Divine. Swami Sivananda has written *'That which separates you from God is Ego. Ego is like a wall between you and God. As soon as ego dissolves you come face to face with God.'*

In our normal day to day dealing, we associate the word ego with 'Ahamkara' only. However, from the yogic and spiritual point of view the word 'Ego' has a very wide connotation. From the point of view of yoga psychology the word ego means 'Separated I' i.e. your feeling of separation from others, from God, from the whole existence. 'Ahamkara' is one of the offshoots of this wider aspect of 'ego' where you want to feel important, superior compared to others, where you want to prove to others that *'I am something'*. 'Ahamkara' in other words is associated with feeling of superiority, importance and pride.

However, not only 'Ahamkara' but all other evils and vikaras also emanate from our feeling of separateness whether it is selfishness, greed, insecurity, fear, attachment, anger, desires. According to yoga psychology 'Ego' is the root vikara, root of all the evils of various kinds which we find in human beings.

As explained earlier, *this root vikara (ego) is associated with our feeling of separateness which is manifested in our day to day life in our feelings of 'I' and 'mine'.* The more the noise of 'I' and 'mine' in our life, the more the separateness and the more the ego we have. More the ego, the more narrow our personality and consciousness becomes and in this state we tend to view everything from a narrow perspective and not as it really is.

There is a saying by the great sage 'Vyasa' in the Mahabharata which says that the two terms or two words constitute bondage and two words constitute liberation. *The two words 'I' and 'Mine' constitute the bondage of the individual soul.* As long as one is caught in this 'I' and 'Mine' business, his state will be a sorry state. There will be now laughing, now weeping; now up, now down; now very loving, now very hating—all conflict and clash. As long as he is caught in the vice-like grip of the two

123

words 'I' and 'Mine' this will be his fate. And what are the twin terms that constitute liberation? *'Not I, Not Mine' these two terms constitute liberation, constitute freedom.* These two terms give ultimate peace and joy and all problems come to an end. The tribulations of the soul, of the spirit, of the individual being, are over.

Ego is also termed as 'false I'. As our ego or 'false I' expands, our original 'I' or pure 'I' recedes in the background. The purpose of all Yoga and spiritual practices is the demolition of 'false I' and emergence of pure or real 'I'. We can also understand in this way that as ego increases, our basic sense of I-ness or identity gets contracted which we call 'false I'. Similarly as ego decreases, our basic sense of I-ness or our identity expands which we refer to as emergence of pure 'I'.

As our identity expands or our 'I' undergoes expansion, we feel oneness with everybody and with the whole creation and this leads to emergence of all positive qualities in us. There can't be any conflict or friction with anything in this state.

As on now you consider yourself 'somebody' but as 'I' expands and becomes more and more pure, your feeling of superiority and pride decreases and when you reach to the highest state of consciousness (i.e. fullest expansion of I), you feel nobody as if you are almost not. There is not the slightest feeling that 'you are something'. It is very rightly said in our Scriptures that *'As long as you are there (i.e. ego is there), God can't be. Only when you are not there, God can be. Both can't live together'.* So for attaining God, you will have to lose yourself (i.e. ego). People don't attain God because they don't want to lose themselves. They are not ready to become *'no-*

body'. And this feeling of 'nobody' spontaneously makes you 'everybody' without any effort on your part.

This becoming of 'nobody' or loss of ego is not a state of emptiness or boredom as people misinterpret. It is rather a state of indescribable bliss, joy, peace. It is with this awareness of pure 'I' that the great Shankaracharya proclaimed 'Aham Brahmasmi' i.e. 'I am God'. This awareness of Divinity emanates in complete loss of ego when pure 'I' shines in you.

We do yoga and meditation just to know this pure 'I' or pure consciousness. As we see it more and more, we become transformed. It is this awareness which removes all our suffering and delusion. It can also be called our true and original nature or our innermost consciousness. Our ego or false 'I' is simply a superimposition over our original nature and is not a permanent part of us and can be discarded as soon as we wake up from our sleep of ignorance.

Ego is always associated with feeling of 'I' and 'mine'

❑ ❑ ❑

125

5

Food for Thoughts

- When we become the master of our mind, nothing good or bad will work upon us. There is no more slavery for us. We will be free from the bondage of anything.
- A man can achieve anything which he can conceive in his mind.
- In your entire life span, you can change only one person and that is yourself.
- It is doubtful that you can change the world but you can certainly change yourself.
- Happiness is neither fulfillment of desires nor suppression of desires. It is overcoming the desires.
- There is no problem in the world which is greater than the strength of your mind.
- Once you surrender yourself to God, there is no limit to what you can achieve.
- Your happiness should be in your hands and not in others'.
- Truth has a power which sustains all the trials and tests of life.
- Truth will always remain truth even if there is not a single follower of it.
- When you realize that you know very little then you are fit for learning.
- A man is judged by every small thing he does. Big things are not necessary for the evaluation of a person.
- You deserve the best of everything in life. It is not your desire but is your right as a divine child of God. So never

compromise in doing or accepting anything which is less than the best.

- Spirituality doesn't mean non-possession of things. It only means non-attachment. A king possessing enormous wealth may be totally unattached while a beggar with torn clothes may be a highly attached person.
- Strictness for oneself and liberality for others is the real greatness.
- Greatest man is he who is the servant of all.
- Truth can never be destroyed. It can only be temporarily subsided. Truth contains a force which does not rest until it is revealed.
- Untruth can never stand because of the inherent weakness associated with it. It has to fall one day.
- The busiest man has the greatest leisure.
- Final say in every matter is of God and not of yours. The freedom given to you is only in the performance of actions but not in the results.
- Ego is the greatest barrier between you and God. It acts like a wall between you and God. Once ego dissolves, you come face to face with God.
- Spirituality doesn't mean leaving the world and actions and going into solitude. It only means a change of attitude while doing the same *karmas* and living in the same world.
- There is always a power with you which is greater than all the odds which can ever come to you in your life.
- The best way to keep yourself happy is to ensure that others are happy.
- Nobody can exercise any power upon you unless you allow him to do so.
- The greatest fear to a man in the world comes from himself only and not from any outside source.
- If you have a determined mind backed by firm faith in God, it is impossible for you not to achieve your goal.

127

- If you like to win but think you can't, it is almost certain that you won't. Such is the power of thought.
- Nothing in this universe can affect or frighten you, unless your mind allows itself to be affected. Such is the power of mind.
- Mind is your greatest friend as well as your biggest enemy. If you use it properly, it is your best friend; if you misuse it, it is your greatest enemy.
- Don't demand material things from God. Your demands only have become a barrier between you and God. Instead just thank God for whatever you have got.
- Purpose of life is not to die one day. You have to fulfill some aim here.
- One ounce of practice is better than tons of theory.
- The degree of your surrender to God decides the extent to which you will receive help from God. If your surrender is total then everything will be done by God for you.
- God is simple. All other things are complex.
- World is meant for our use and not for possession. It is to be used only as a means to achieve our ends.
- Real preaching is through behaviour and conduct and not by words. Effect of former is ten times greater than that of the latter.
- All our actions should give the reflection of our original nature which is ever pure and blissful. All our actions should become divinized.
- A joyous spirit will always find reasons to be happy in any circumstances. A gloomy spirit will always find reasons to be unhappy in any circumstances.
- For doing something time will never be separately available to you. It will have to be carved out from the same 24 hours, if you want to do something.
- When you surrender to God, you have a kind of assurance that whatever you need or wish, will certainly come to you and that there is no question about its non-receiving.

- If you can take care of things which are in your hand, things which are not in your hand will be automatically taken care of.
- Nobody can be helped unless he wants to be helped. Desire and will are the prime requirements for the progress.
- The fears which we experience in the outside world come from our inside only, although it doesn't appear to be so. By deep contemplation you may realize that you yourself are the source of your fears.
- If your demand is sincere and is in conformity with cosmic order, supply will certainly come to you. If a thing doesn't exist in the universe, it will be created for you.
- Sickness is more in mind than in the body. You can't be sick until you feel sick.
- No one can make you happy except you yourself.
- No one was ever really taught by another. Each of us has to teach himself in the long run. External teacher only arouses the internal teacher.
- Anger, provocation, irritation only shows that instead of being the master, we are still the slaves of our lower mind (also called animal mind or automatic mind).
- Know that you are separated entirely from the world though you are in the world. Then no action will have any binding effect on you.
- You can see in others only what is in yourself. You can't see the faults in others unless the same faults are in yourself.
- The problems and sufferings in our life are like the tests and exams in the school of life to teach us certain lessons and to tell us where we stand.
- World is a theatre or a stage where we all are actors playing our designated roles. How well we play our roles is only important and not the role itself. In different births we may be given different types of roles to enable us to grow in various directions.
- The more you will resist sufferings and miseries in life, the more they will trouble you; the more you accept them, the more easily they will leave you.

- You can be to others only what you are to yourself. If you are honest with yourself, you will be honest to others as well.
- True spirituality goes beyond all religions.
- Money can give you everything except happiness. It has the power to make you miserable in comforts.
- Whatever is within us, the same appears to us in the outside world. Hence every person makes his own world which is different from each other.
- Real pleasure is in giving or sacrificing and not in receiving.
- Accepting and recognizing your weaknesses is the first step for removing them.
- You are not a helpless creature revolving endlessly in the wheel of destiny. You have the power by which you can neutralize, partly or fully, the effect of destiny on you. *What you have done, you can undo also.*
- Unless you are ready to accept responsibility for the conditions in which you are, there is very little which can be done to change your conditions.
- *If you want to work most efficiently but with least stress, work as a servant of God* considering every work entrusted to you by the divine (GOD).
- If you can just walk towards God, He will run to you. If we are ready to take one step towards him, He is ready to take two steps towards us.
- Don't overstress yourself by taking responsibilities of those things which are not in your hands. Leave the results of everything on God and become light. You are simply an humble worker and not the decision maker or destiny maker which is totally God's job.
- Wise men learn from fools more than what fools learn from them.
- Whatever we do, God should be in front of us. In this '*mela*' of the world, we are safe only so long as we are moving with our hands in His hands. As soon as our hands slip, we get lost in this 'mela' and are left in a highly miserable and confused state.

- Have all that you want and even more but try not to have any idea of proprietorship or possessorship.
- Ideas of respect and acceptance of all religions are not contradictory but complementary to each other. Every religion reinforces another religion.
- Any work or action that doesn't place God at the top, is incomplete. Without associating God in your work, there is no guarantee for success. You never know from which quarter disaster may strike.
- If you have taken the first step, you are likely to take the last step also. Well begun is half done.
- The person who has learnt to bow, has almost reached to God.
- Make God your partner and associate Him in everything you do. There is nothing which you can't do with the help of God.
- A person's mental reaction to an event is more important than the event itself. However hard the realities of life may be, they are not as important as our attitude towards them.
- The person who is same in thought, word and deed is only fit to be a realized soul.
- Silence is the hardest argument which can sometimes be offered to your opponent.
- No matter at what stage you are, there is always a scope for further advancement.
- Nothing goes in vain in this world. Even a thought you think, a word you speak, make a definite impact on the whole universe, howsoever infinitesimal it may be.
- The person who sees the kind hand of God even in miseries and sufferings is the true recipient of His grace.
- Your worst difficulties are your best opportunities.
- The purpose of spiritual development is to rise above the limitations of mundane life.
- For a true spiritual seeker, there is nothing which is low or high, trivial or important. Everything and every occasion is an opportunity for him in the path of liberation.

- Mind is the most powerful thing in this world. One who has fully conquered his mind has all the powers at his command. Whatever he says becomes words of scriptures. Wherever he goes becomes a place for pilgrimage.

- World is a laboratory where we do various types of experiments to learn various things and are also tested off and on by facing various trials which are offered to us.

- If you want to avoid pains, you will have to avoid pleasures also.

- The pleasure and joy which we want to enjoy from the body and the world, considering them as real, are in reality only nightmares.

- Appearance of problems and difficulties and their disappearance after sometime are like the day following night. One should tolerate them patiently without getting upset.

- Never think that you are inferior to anybody and never think that you are superior to anybody. All differences are unreal.

- Mind is a mysterious something which is really nothing but does everything. There is nothing in all the three worlds which is not its creation. Creation, existence, and dissolution of this universe are projections of this mysterious mind.

- One who is neither unduly elated by success nor grieved by sorrow, who is equipoised in most adverse circum-stances, in praise and censure, in wealth and poverty, rather in all conditions of life, ever conscious of his real nature unaffected by the play of the elements, is a perfect person.

- The person who has controlled his mind has almost attained God.

- When you are able to overcome worldly pleasures and pains, attractions and repulsion, you don't experience simply a blank or void, you experience a spiritual awakening in yourself.

- We always think that by changing this or that condition, we will be in a more comfortable position in this world. But in the new conditions also we find ourselves surrounded by new problems. Unless we realize that source of happiness is within us, we may live anywhere and in whatever conditions, we will always be stressed.

- The more we involve in worldly pleasures and enjoyments, the more we get bound and entangled and the more difficult it becomes for us to be free from them and get liberated.

- Once you know the truth of life, you cease to see the differences in the world. There is no difference between a friend and a foe, big and small, rich and poor, strong and weak, and neighbour and common man. All are seen as the children of God and all are actors in the world playing different roles.

- A person, who is stabilized in soul consciousness and God consciousness, enjoys all worldly things and objects of pleasure in a detached manner. For him there is no difference between Gold and stone.

- If I like praise, it means I can be easily hurt by defamation.

- You can give to others only what is inside you. If you have anger, irritation, hatred inside you, you will give the same to others.

- A child always remains tension free. Similarly you can also be tension free if you consider yourself as the child of God.

- The greatest men of the world also had only twenty four hours in a day like you have. They hadn't any more time than you for becoming great.

- World is a great training school where we train ourselves by learning various lessons in the form of facing variable conditions, events, circumstances, joys and sorrows, etc.

❏ ❏ ❏

Check Your Stress Index?

Stress is difficult to understand. The emotional chaos it causes can make our daily lives miserable. It also decreases our physical health, sometimes drastically. Strangely, we are not always aware that we are under stress.

How high is your Stress Index? Find out by scoring your answers to the questions below.

Score 1 for each "Yes" and 0 for each "No".

DO YOU FREQUENTLY	YES	NO
Neglect diet?		
Try to do everything yourself?		
Blow up easily?		
Seek unrealistic goals?		
Fail to see the humour in situations others find funny?		
Act rude?		
Make a "big deal" of everything?		
Look to other people to make things happen?		
Complain you are disorganized?		
Avoid people whose ideas are different from your own?		
Keeps everything inside?		
Neglect exercise?		
Have few supportive relationships?		
Use sleeping pills and tranquilizers without a doctor's approval?		
Get too little rest?		
Get angry when you are kept waiting?		
Ignore stress symptoms?		
Try to delay your thing?		
Think there is only one right way to do something?		
Fail to build relaxation time into your day?		
Gossip?		
Race through the day?		
Spend a lot of time complaining about the past?		
Fail to get a break from noise and crowds?		
TOTAL YOUR SCORE		

What Your Score Means:

1-6: There are few hassles in your life. Do not avoid problems and shy away from challenges.

7-13: You have got your life in fairly good control. Work on the choices and habits that could still be causing you some unnecessary stress in your life.

14-20: You are approaching the danger zone. You may well be suffering stress-related symptoms and your relationships could be strained. Think carefully about choices you have made and take relaxation breaks everyday.

Above 20: Emergency! You must stop now, re-think how you are living, change your attitudes, and pay careful attention to diet, exercise, and relaxation.

❑ ❑ ❑